C000255613

NEW WELSH READER

PLACE MARKERS

NONFICTION

Winners in the New Welsh Writing Awards 2021 Rheidol Prize for Prose with a Welsh Theme or Setting

4   **Landmark** Elizabeth Griffiths

15   **Archipelago** Rhiannon Hooson

26   **Reading the Signs** Jasmine Donahaye

70   **Tales of Cariad County** Tony Brown on the interwar and postwar stories of Nigel Heseltine

FICTION

Winners in the New Welsh Writing Awards 2021 Rheidol Prize for Prose with a Welsh Theme or Setting

35   **The Rebeccas** Jack Harris

41   **Festival of the Ghost** João Morais

50   **The Kaiser and the River** Sybilla Harvey

POETRY

62   **Memory Clinic I** Steven Hastings

62   **I Can't Complain (Ten Reasons Why)** Steven Hastings

67   **Pet** Stuart Pickford

68   **We Were the Last of the Creative Writing Society** Suzannah Evans

New Welsh Reader
New Welsh Review Ltd
PO Box 170, Aberystwyth, SY23 1WZ
Telephone: 01970 628410
www.newwelshreview.com

Editor:
Gwen Davies
editor@newwelshreview.com

Administration & Finance Officer:
Bronwen Williams
admin@newwelshreview.com

Marketing & Publicity Officer:
Julia Forster
marketing@newwelshreview.com

Management Board:
Ali Anwar, Gwen Davies (Director),
Andrew Green (Director, Chair), Ruth
Killick, David Michael (Treasurer),
Matthew Francis, Emily Blewitt (Poetry
Subs Editor, Vice-Chair)

Aberystwyth University Partnership:
Natalia Elliot, Tayler Walters, Amy Aed

**Sponsor of the New Welsh Writing
Awards:** RS Powell

Design: Ingleby Davies Design

Main images: Cover, Garway Hill,
Hereford (Richard Fullbrook / Unsplash),
Contents (top), Zebra Finches (Chocopie
/ Shutterstock), Contents (right),
Stonewall Hill near Presteigne (Rhiannon
Hooson).

Host: Aberystwyth University

ISBN: 9781913830083
ISSN: 09542116

Views expressed in NWR are the authors'
own and do not necessarily reflect the
opinions of either editor or board.

The New Welsh Review Ltd publishes with
the financial support of the Books Council
of Wales, and is hosted by Aberystwyth
University's Department of English &
Creative Writing. The New Welsh Review
Ltd was established in 1988 by Academi
(now Literature Wales) and the Association
for Welsh Writing in English. *New Welsh
Reader* is New Welsh Review's print (and
digital) magazine for creative work. We
also publish monthly roundups of online
content, including reviews, comment and
poetry, and at least one book annually on
the New Welsh Rarebyte imprint, run a
writing competition (New Welsh Writing
Awards), and improve diversity in the UK
publishing industry by hosting student
work placements.

Mae croeso ichi ohebu â'r golygydd
yn Gymraeg.

Patrons: Belinda Humfrey, Owen Sheers

Ariennir gan
Lywodraeth Cymru
Funded by
Welsh Government

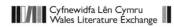

SIGN UP!

Our new website can be browsed by category, theme tag or title and is now a one-stop shop for our ePub formats and fully searchable digital archive, books, offers and more. New-look digital editions are fully searchable, have a page-turning feature and include complete text to speech (TTS) element as standard.

NEW WELSH REVIEW REVIEWS & COMMENT

Road Trip Marvin Thompson (Peepal Tree). **Pam Thompson** recommends a compassionate, complex poetry collection of the Windrush generation and rural Gwent.

The Cormorant Stephen Gregory (Parthian). **Laura Wainwright** is intrigued by a classic horror novel in which the bird is an avatar of male vulnerabilities.

Catallus: Shibari Carmina Isobel Williams, text & illustrations (Carcanet). **Katrina Naomi** explores what Japanese bondage at a London fetish club brings to an adaptation of the Roman poet.

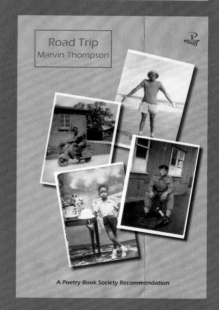

A Poetry Book Society Recommendation

NEW WELSH READER 128 ESSAYS, MEMOIR, STORIES, POETRY

'The Silence Project' Story by **Carole Hailey**

'Over-exposed' Photo-landscape essay by **Yvonne Reddick**

'Bass in the Blood' Rural rave-culture memoir by **Jodie Bond**

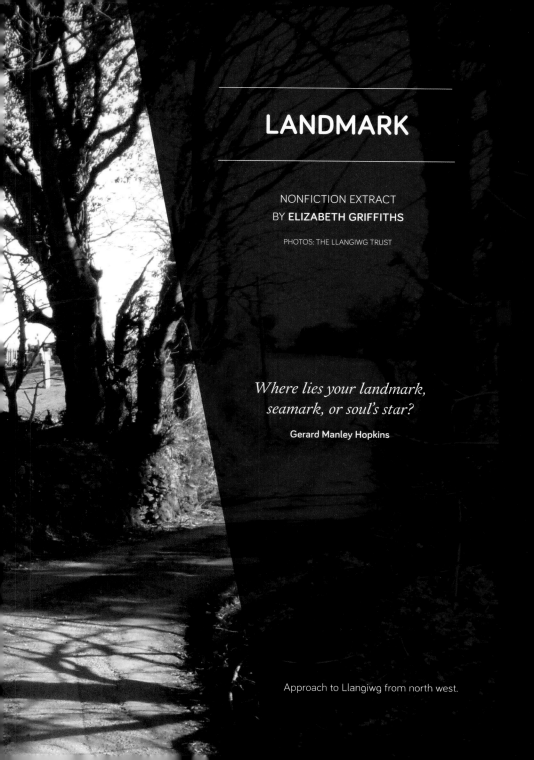

LANDMARK

NONFICTION EXTRACT
BY **ELIZABETH GRIFFITHS**

PHOTOS: THE LLANGIWG TRUST

Where lies your landmark,
seamark, or soul's star?

Gerard Manley Hopkins

Approach to Llangiwg from north west.

December 8th, 2019. On these stormy nights, as the wet and wind slap around our bungalow beneath the east coast dunes, my mind is tethered to an ancient hilltop tower not far from the sea at Swansea: how is it bearing up to the weather? Storm Atiyah, the first of the winter season, has been hitting the west coast hard; damage is forecast in Wales. Will the rain invade the tower, as it does when the wind drives in a certain direction? What about that slipped roof tile I need to get fixed? The weather, climate change, is much on everyone's mind these days, and here on the Lincolnshire coast we have our own small worries. Will the prospect of rising sea levels deter people from buying our bungalow when we try to sell it next year? Will we get through another winter without a breach in the sea defences? How and when will we get back to Wales, and that tower?

IT'S THE TOWER I SEE WHEN I THINK OF LLANGIWG; THE TOWER FIRST, without the larger, rectangular structure it's attached to, which is the nave of a church. Here, so the tradition goes, a sixth-century holy man named Ciwg established his mission above the Swansea Valley. I never expected to inherit this building from my mother, and nor did she expect it, even though she owned it, on paper at least. After she bought it from the Church in Wales in 2007, she handed it over on a century-long lease to a community charity, so that it would be looked after well beyond my lifetime. I never imagined losing sleep over it.

In my mind's eye, the tower always rears up from the north-west, its dark stone walls and crenellated top rising through trees from the lane below. At first glance, it looks like a small fort, or castle remnant, standing on the crest of the Barley, a hill nearly 700 feet above sea level. But this impression is lost as you track up and round to the south and view the front of the church entire. Against the long nave, the tower now looks as if it should be taller, which it almost certainly was, long ago. Its unmistakable westward lean explains why, at some point, it was reduced in height for safety.

Working the fields on Barley Hill, date unknown, possibly early-mid twentieth century.

'Don't worry, it's not going anywhere,' a local surveyor told me as I peered up at it nervously, one dank February day in 2019. 'Historic settlement,' he said, 'centuries ago.'

Close up, the impression of a fortification returns. It's the putlog holes that get to me – small square apertures that pierce those ultra-thick walls like eyes. They put you in mind of a bygone age of defence and attack, although they exist for the practical purpose of receiving the ends of scaffolding poles (putlogs), a method used by the ancient Romans. Rising four-square from the ground, St Ciwg's tower has a particularly stolid, cubic feel, and always strikes me as older than the rest of the building, though experts at the Royal Commission on the Ancient and Historical Monuments of Wales say that the whole church appears to be of the same late medieval re-build, generally believed to be c 1500. 'But there are Norman remnants,' I remember my mother telling me, quick to point it out. 'The tower has Norman remnants.'

According to the Royal Commission, the tower is 'an extravagance, existing simply to house a ring of bells... an embellishment that most upland churches would have wanted but few managed to achieve.' In the

Holy well, Llangiwg churchyard.

days when communities populated the hills rather than the valleys, it must have been quite a landmark, especially when it was taller. Yet you can drive towards Llangiwg along any of the valley roads or over the neighbouring Gwrhyd mountain without seeing it at all, from any angle. Unlike the churches in Lincolnshire, which can be viewed across the county's plains and undulations for miles around, like points on a map, St Ciwg's location – isolated, partially wooded and relatively remote – seems to hide itself until you're right upon it, whatever your approach, north, south, east or west.

My mother and I last spent time together there in May 2017, a day warm enough for my sister and brother-in-law to stretch out and sun themselves by the holy well, while my mother and I took a slow, quiet walk up the incline behind the church. Arm in arm, we waded through long grasses and late bluebells between the graveyard's older stones and slabs that lean or lie almost hidden in the overgrowth. My mother was still relying heavily on a stick after a recent hip operation, yet her eyes darted about, checking for changes – to the church roof with its inappropriate modern tiles, the walls with their ghostly blocked-in Tudor windows, and the rambling semi-wild grounds, which were awaiting their summer cut after the plants had flowered. It was a while since she'd been able to drive over independently from her home in Ystradgynlais, a twenty-minute trip across the Gwrhyd, and she was keen to make the most of this visit. On we ploughed, up into the rockier, bracken-covered reaches of the churchyard, till we stopped at its eastern boundary and the spot where this llan (literally, a settlement or enclosure) may have originated.

There's precious little on record about the development of the church over the centuries; the building itself has to be our best guide for that. According to the only book available on St Ciwg's, published by the Friends of Llangiwg in 2009, the few documents that existed were destroyed in a fire. Research into the parish of Llangiwg over the last half millenium has yielded details of tithes, populations, incumbents, and so on. But it's only in a letter written in 1697 by the then incumbent, Thomas Morgan, that we gain, perhaps, a tantalising glimpse of Llangiwg's beginnings. 'Kiwg,' writes Morgan, was by tradition 'an Hermit and saint who had his cell in a rock anext to the Church yard over which rock there is at this day a little house built for the parish Clerk called Y Maen Dy, not a stately Edifice, but as it were a [illegible word] imbraceing the cell.'

That afternoon my mother and I spent several minutes regarding the ivy-covered ruin of this building next to the churchyard, which I know she coveted as an important part of the site, and hoped might one day be investigated and integrated into the whole. By the nineteenth century, this clerk's house had become a pub, known as the Maendy, which churchgoers used to frequent after morning service. Some of the congregation would play ball games against the tower too, and other sports outside the churchyard, a picture which chimes with Thomas Morgan's quaint observation that the inhabitants of his day were 'strong active people at Runing, Vaulting, gameing etc.'

Morgan's letter confirms that, by the end of the seventeenth century, parishioners no longer held 'their wakes' (the saint's feast day celebrations)

Ruin of Maendy pub, east of churchyard, by tradition the site of Ciwg's cell

at St Peter's Tide on June 29th – this custom was now 'out of use' – and nor, according to relatives of those earlier parishioners, did pilgrims come from afar to worship 'afore Kuke's cell, with candles or torches burning, to perform their Devotion, or present their prayers and offerings to that Saint.' The popular medieval cult of saints encouraged by the Catholic church – which may have made it financially possible to restore buildings like St Ciwg's in the preceding centuries – appears to have been well past its heyday, even though the decline in Catholic rituals after the Reformation was probably seen later in Wales than elsewhere. No longer, it seems, were the saints regarded with such enthusiasm as personal guardians, protectors, friends.

January 1st, 2020

'*Wel dyma ni'n dwad, / Gyfeillion diniwad, / I ofyn am gennad i canu….*'
(Well here we come, / Innocent friends, / To ask may we have leave to sing….)

Videos of last night's Mari Lwyd celebration at Llangiwg have come through on WhatsApp, the church flickering with candlelight and decked out with winter greenery. The future of the old place may still be precarious, but the New Year has been seen in as usual, with 'pwnco' [singing rhymes on the doorstep to attain entry] and songs and a baubled horse's skull – the mischievous Mari. The traditional tunes and jokes never fail to work their innocent magic. Mum never missed the Mari Lwyd, which still draws quite a crowd – there were about sixty, including the troupe of musicians, singers and mummers, who made it up the narrow country lanes as it was getting dark. The car park was chockablock. People say there's nothing like the atmosphere at Llangiwg for enacting this strange, ancient, pre-Christian ritual, in which a horse comes to life in the dead of winter, signifying – what exactly? Re-birth? The permeability between the worlds of the living and of the dead? It may have links with Celtic mythology, but nobody really knows. My cousin uncovered Llangiwg's old electric organ, unused for many years, and brought it back to life – she found it 'not too bad, only a bit of a background dirge'. At the end of the evening, everyone had to wait for a tractor to pull out a 4x4 which had slipped into a ditch off the rain-soaked verge, blocking the road. Will the Mari bring us good fortune in the coming year?

My mother put in a bid for St Ciwg's because she was 'cross' with the Church in Wales for selling it, so someone told me at her funeral. I was surprised. If there was one word I never associated with my mother it was 'judgmental'. It's true that the church was very much on 'her patch', although until she told me she wanted to buy it for the community, I'd never heard about it. She had grown up only a few miles away, the child of a coal-mining district on the valley floor. She came from an ordinary small street, from a family preoccupied with the daily grind of running a business. I can see now that to scramble up the valley side to Llangiwg at the end of a school afternoon in Pontardawe was to enter another world. There was the natural beauty of the place, for one thing – the open space, the elevation, fresh air, quiet. Generations of children, I'm sure, even to this day, discover a storybook magic about finding themselves up there, alone or with a friend, and exploring the unkempt churchyard where there are plenty of curiosities, not only among the gravestones, but also beneath the coiled branches of the ancient yew or on the slope below the tower, where the natural spring that feeds the holy well often gushes out through a pipe in the boundary wall, splashing all over the road.

For my mother, I think the attraction went beyond this, even though she was barely in her teens when she first wandered around the church-yard with her schoolfriend, Margaret. She sensed something there, picked up a resonance, a vibration, an energy, call it what you will. 'The place had presence, it spoke to me,' she wrote simply, when asked to explain why she became involved with Llangiwg, nearly sixty years later. She experienced a silence and a stillness she hadn't known before, in the churchyard as much as the church. 'If the church were to fall into decay,' she wrote elsewhere, 'it wouldn't make any difference, Llangiwg would still be a special place.'

She never spoke of attending church services at Llangiwg as a young-ster or adult. Her family, like many others, was a split church/chapel household, her father attending Tabernacl Independent Chapel and her mother, the local Victorian parish church. As industrialisation trans-formed the Swansea Valley in the nineteenth century, new churches and chapels had gradually proliferated across the valley floor to serve the growing towns and villages, so there was no need for people to trek uphill to Llangiwg. In the 1860s, the churchyard, by virtue of its remote-ness, became the only place for miles around where cholera victims were laid to rest, because other churches refused to take them; it was here too that the poor of Pontardawe Workhouse were buried in paupers' graves. In 1872, with the fall-off in passing traffic, the Maendy pub finally closed its doors.

In spite of these changes, and the long general decline in church attendance in the latter part of the twentieth century, St Ciwg's sur-vived for well over another hundred years, until 2003, when it was closed for good and deconsecrated. Inevitable, you might think. Even so, my mother was 'cross' when she saw the For Sale notice in the local paper a few years later. In her notebooks, the phrases 'mother church of the parish' and 'oldest building in the borough' are jotted down with underlines, as if she felt it was wrong to cast off such a place, like some disadvantaged elderly relative. Elsewhere among her papers, I've come across publicity material used about ten years ago to launch a restora-tion appeal for the church: *Hiraeth am Gymru a'i hên drysor...* runs the heading. *A longing for Wales and its old treasure....* I've tried to find out if this is a quotation, without success. *Trysor...* 'Old treasure'? I wondered, rather stupidly, when I first glanced at these words. Heritage, of course.

Up to then, I hadn't shared my mother's lifelong passion for history; I didn't really understand it. It was a subject she had studied at college, but more than that, it was an interest she pursued in everyday life, whether tracing the family tree, talking to elderly relatives, visiting old buildings,

View west, from top of tower.

taking part in historical re-enactments at festivals or running an oral history project. Even when she worked for a while as a mental health nurse at the Mid Wales Hospital in Talgarth, Powys, she loved to listen to and privately record the life stories of her patients. The source of my mother's strong feelings about Llangiwg arose, I think, not only from a sensitivity to the numinous, but also an instinct about the power of tradition, of heritage.

Elizabeth Griffiths grew up in west Wales, and is hoping to return to live in Wales soon, after spending twenty years next to the North Sea in Lincolnshire. She studied at St David's University College, Lampeter, and trained as a journalist on the *Barry and District News* in South Glamorgan, winning the Law Society graduate prize and the NCTJ Bath and West special merit prize. While living in Pembrokeshire in the 1990s, she had several short stories published, one of which was included in Parthian's fiction anthology, *Mama's Baby (Papa's Maybe): New Welsh Short Fiction*. In 2018, she completed a Creative Writing MA at Swansea University, and in 2019 was highly commended in the New Welsh Writing Awards for a memoir of her grandfather, 'Abel Thomas and Sons Butter Merchants Ltd', which was subsequently published in *New Welsh Reader*. This extract is from 'Landmark: The Essay', her highly commended entry in the New Welsh Writing Awards 2021 Rheidol Prize for Prose with a Welsh Theme or Setting. llangiwgtrust.org

ARCHIPELAGO

NONFICTION EXTRACT BY **RHIANNON HOOSON**

When my mother left Carmarthen for Jamaica, they scraped the Welsh off her like cleaning a window. She was five. She grew up walking the rail tracks with her Dats, where he'd worked all his life, or by the Tywy where her great uncle, old man Elias, floated coracles like prayers across the river. She grew up watching her Mams knuckle soft curranted dough in the big bread bowl to make hot cross buns.

Then Jamaica. Her father taught at an army school there. I think of her as a child putting on a blindfold for a game, spinning and spinning, then removing it to find herself in a different place altogether.

It was the late fifties. In the officers' club with her friend Penny she drank fizzy pop by the pool. Weekends, they would drive out to Dunn's River Falls and swim in the warm sea and the cold river. From the window of their neat new bungalow she would look down across the evening garden where huge toads lined the lawn, and watch their maid, Hazel, wring the neck of a chicken.

I think of deep green shadows and bright light. I think of the way the sun bleached her brown hair blond. Sometimes quakes would mean the earth shook its back beneath her. She talked about that with me, later. About how the surface of the road rippled like something living, and the church bell rang.

*

On Stonewall Hill, spring starts with a biting wind and ranks of snowdrops that push their way through the bleached and tangled grasses of the verge. The air is never quiet: always the wind, always the colony of crows calling to one another, always the sound of the seasons announcing themselves in endless procession.

It is a high hill, the tallest around, but not so tall that trees might shun it. At its summit, a plateau that widens into windblown fields, hidden hollows, a network of narrow lanes and tracks that all lead, eventually, down. Along one of these lanes, which climbs up out of the valley of the River Lugg, a humble, tumbledown stone wall follows the border between England and Wales, giving the hill its name. It was already built when the Act of Union decided the border in 1536. It's along this lane that I like to walk – up along the Welsh side, back along the English, my little dog, Pippin, and I.

In high places, I feel a sort of momentum driving me forward, one foot then the other, a pulse in the ground beneath me. Even the air seems tall above the crown of my head, opening into a bleached blueness where red kites wheel and cry. It is a vantage point into the year, and into two countries; a borderland where you can stand in a quiet sunny lane, and see from the Wrekin in the north to Pen y Fan in the south. And in the spring, the whole of Herefordshire opens to the eye, a great bowl brimming with apple blossom all the way to the Malvern Hills.

The Malverns; Moelfryn. Bare hill. Along the border Welsh spills onto the English map, worn away to easy syllables on cottage gates and farm tracks and crossroads. Nearby in Herefordshire you can drive along Rhyse Lane which floods every winter, to the Leen, where a white bull stamps behind a new strong gate, or else follow the River Arrow or Arwy, to where it slides past Penrhos, where they make expensive gin now that sells in the shops of Hereford and Ludlow.

Even after the snowdrops, snow lingers up on the hill. There are banks of it riddled with hollows well into spring, and under the smell of growing things and of greenery, its cold high note pierces the air as shrill as the cry of a buzzard. Now only one drift is left, shallowing into the grass behind a wide hedge more bramble than hawthorn, having found the spot the sun won't reach until later in the year. We skim the edge of the snowdrift, its gritty crystals parting to let the grass through and crunching to nothing under the dog's paws.

Soon enough, anemones will be blooming in the quiet wood. Already the daisies have opened, and we follow a blackbird from perch to perch along the lane, Pippin tugging to chase it, until as a tractor passes we lose sight of it – only to spot its yellow beak against the white of the black-thorn tree, its delicate feet gripping the branch between two thorns. The colour of iron, I think. The colour of iron against a softness of blossom: in this way winter passes into spring. I give the dog a biscuit from my pocket.

Ahead of me my own shadow, with its head in the tangled verge, watches the path the year takes through a half-wild space.

*

I grow up in Radnorshire, further into Wales, in a succession of squat old houses that lean from their surroundings like outcrops of rock. There are always barns and old trees and various tracks cut into the hillsides, and woods with names like Red Wood, and North Wood, and Top Wood. There is always a river. There are lambs in spring, and firewood stacked in the autumn.

We don't farm, but we live on farmland. There are farmers, mostly named John, who come and go with their dogs, opening and shutting gates.

On Fridays at school, a woman comes to teach us Welsh, while we sit cross-legged around her on the brown carpet. I can make all the sounds. They never feel foreign in my mouth. But my Welsh teacher is the only person I have ever heard speaking Welsh.

We learn simple words. Ffordd, pêl, melyn.

Dwi'n hoffi coffi, we say.

At night, my father reads me Ursula LeGuin. He teaches me new words too: *archipelago*, and *archetype*, and *longship*, and *dubious*.

My father knows the names for all the hills. He spends each day on hilltops surveying barrows and hill forts and ruins. He's come from Yorkshire, but he learned the names so that they fit closely against the world. The names for places mean something to him. He teaches me dôl, a meadow, and dolau, meadows. Bryn, a hill, and llan, an enclosure. He is careful with Welsh, as if it is a gift given to him unexpectedly by a stranger.

But the names he uses are not used by anyone we know. They come out skewed from men's mouths who do not like to move their lips or jaw or tongue, who speak like speech at all was forced on them by something external: the government, or their wives; a necessary evil.

When I am seven, we move to a house called Dolau Farm. Everyone else calls it 'dolly'. I hate it. It feels like some subtle insult. I have not played with dolls for years.

*

The weather warms; in a week, on the far side of the hill, where oak woods give way to an abandoned orchard, ramsons fill the air with the smell of garlic and flowers. There was a cottage here once, its stones long swallowed by opportunistic elder trees. It's a good spot for gathering elder blossom for cordial later in the year, but as yet, the trees are shaded only a chartreuse green with new leaves, and in the old orchard, where the trees are drooping under a weight of seasons, a robin is hopping about among the last of the wild daffodils.

I like to stop here and look out across the valley. Once I coaxed a mouse from its hole in the old hedge with morsels of a peanut butter sandwich, but today there's no sign of it. The track that switchbacks up the hill is empty, but in a distant field, a bonfire of the winter's dead wood is burning, and the scent of it reaches me even here.

The scent of woodsmoke and water. It makes me think of the builders' yard by the canal in Lancaster, when I was desperate to find something of the countryside in my little city, and found a strange solace in the smell of burning wood drifting across the water.

Each moment on the hill unfolds into a hundred more. The more intimately I come to know this little patch of ground, the more intricate its map of associated memories and thoughts becomes. Its rhythms and my own are not a regular beat to learn but an ever-changing complexity, marked not by a regiment of months but a progression of moments –

Here: In spring, we come upon two big hares on the path through the wood, not boxing but in consultation between the shadows of tall oaks, their ears ragged, their whiskers golden in the light.

Or here: It is raining. The track is a river, and I wade ankle deep while lambs, gathered in a boisterous gang, track my progress from the primrose-covered bank. I can almost hear them laughing.

Down from the hill, I make tea and get out the map. It's old, and the names on it are unfamiliar even if the landscape is the one I know: the lower slopes of the hill were home to vanished villages, once. A life, long since abandoned by people who moved down to an easier living in the towns and valleys. Ranks of medieval cottages and a market square now ploughed under the black earth.

I can see it so clearly: In winter the air at the turn in the river was blue with smoke, and the patch of elders was full of old women in blue and black and red, gossiping as they cut dead wood for the fires. Sometimes, ice froze across the river, and the young folk tied bones to their boots and skated where, in summer, they had fished for trout among the mayflies. The old orchard spilled red apples across the frosty grass. Already the priory was empty, its great walls sprouting rooks and birch saplings. And sometimes, the priory is a ruin, only one wall left standing, and the village is centuries vanished, and the river runs cold and slow, and the road is empty but for quiet echoes that come up out of the wood in winter, when the air smells faintly of smoke.

*

I am in my twenties. I have not spoken Welsh for a decade. I am starting to get poems published, starting to get booked for gigs. The bio I send out begins *Rhiannon Hooson is a Welsh poet.* I miss Wales so much my heart is sick with it, but I look at the hills picked out in frost by the sharp winter light, and it eases. I feel more at home in Cumbria, where I live, than I did in Lancaster. You couldn't see hills there.

Whenever I tell my name to someone up here, they get a vague, confused look on their face before a relieved smile when they remember: 'Your parents liked Fleetwood Mac, did they?'

No, I say. It's Welsh. I'm Welsh.

But you don't sound Welsh, they say. You don't sound Welsh at all.

I can see they think it is a sort of compliment. I want to tell them I know. That I've never sounded Welsh. That no one 'sounds Welsh' where I'm from, not in the way they mean it.

Sometimes, they will ask, but can you speak Welsh though?

Sometimes, when I say no, they ask me to do the accent anyway.

*

On the hill, there were hedges once, more than there are now, and shade plants still grow in their ghosts, even in the cold clear sun. Heading south down the lane that goes to Stocking Farm, the hill begins to raise its shoulder, until there's shelter enough for a tall hedge of hawthorn and larch and rowans that spill vermillion berries across the tarmac in autumn. The lane goes down past the Warren, and Goat House, where a line of desiccated moles hang from a fence, rattling in the breeze, their little lives shrunk to nothing.

Here, where the stump of a footpath sign has again been chainsawed level with the hedge, there's an attenuated view east into the gulley that runs down deeper into England, towards Willey Hall. Between alder trees that lean at odd angles, water begins as a sound, and only further down, emerges as some bright, brief thing, a glance between tufts of long grass. The Lime Brook has sources dotted across the eastern side of the hill, between rounded summits of the same massif, each with its own name.

Stonewall Hill becomes Brierley Hill, becomes Reeves Hill, becomes Harley's Mountain, becomes Hell Peak, becomes The Globe, becomes Llan-wen Hill, becomes Hawthorn Hill, becomes Boresford Hill, where above another unnamed tributary of the Lime Brook, the ground undulates gently, earning it a name of its own: The Devil's Ridges. In summer,

wild strawberries stud the steep bank between the lane and the wood there, and woodpeckers echo in the spaces between trees. It isn't that the land is relentlessly plentiful, more that the hill and its skirts lie perfectly balanced on the border between Radnorshire's thin skimmed hills where the ground is good for not much but sheep, and Herefordshire's deep red soil, where apples and hops and strawberries burst readily into the warmer air, and bilberries clutter the forest floor, and the lanes are full of partridges.

'We're on our third harvest in Herefordshire,' a friend used to tease. 'Tipping strawberries into the river, we are.'

Rhiannon Hooson has won major awards for her work, including an Eric Gregory Award from the Society of Authors, and her first book, *The Other City*, was shortlisted for the Wales Book of the Year award. She has performed at literature festivals across the UK, and her work has been featured in *The Guardian*, *Magma*, and *Poetry Wales*, among others. In the last few years, she has been a Literature Wales bursary recipient, a Hay Festival Writer at Work, and the judge of the PENfro festival poetry competition. She has a PhD in poetry from the University of Lancaster, and spent time living and working in Cumbria and Mongolia before settling in the Welsh Marches. This is an extract from 'Archipelago', highly commended in the New Welsh Writing Awards 2021 Rheidol Prize for Prose with a Welsh Theme or Setting.

READING THE SIGNS

NONFICTION EXTRACT BY **JASMINE DONAHAYE**

One for Sorrow

IN THE WAITING ROOM, A MAN IS HOLDING THE EDGES OF HIS NEWSPAPER so tightly that he has crumpled the pages. He stares at the news, his eyes not moving. Somewhere beyond the pale beech veneer door with its heavy steel handle, the woman he loves is stripping off her shirt, undoing her bra, laying them on a chair; she is stepping up to the machine, leaning into it as instructed, trying to relax her arm, which the radiographer places out of the way, like a discarded scarf. She is pulling her other breast away from the descending plate; she winces as the plates meet and this organ of pleasure and nourishment, slack and misshapen, is squeezed flat. She gasps at the surprising grip, and the man she loves is weeping in the waiting room, staring at the page of his paper which he has not yet turned, which he will never turn. What is happening in the world has blurred and cannot be retrieved. All this week and next there will be no news but the static of a radio caught between stations.

In a few minutes, she'll be done. Turning away from the radiographer, she'll hook-and-eye her bra in a strange new modesty, and pull on her shirt. She'll come back through that heavy door and he will stand up, fast, laying down the paper without folding it. They'll go home. He'll make them tea, and they'll drink it together; they will lie down together and make love quietly, mid-morning, not knowing what is to come, whether this autumn, this shit-and-maggots season, is the shit-and-maggots season of their love.

What did they secretly count or note, what private readings and understandings did they create out of what they saw as they drove here this morning? *If the sun breaks through the cloud... if the traffic-light turns green before I count to twenty-five... if there's somewhere to park straight away, then everything's going to be OK; she's going to be all right.* And what dread clutched him when, by the count of twenty-five, the light had not after all changed, nor by thirty, by thirty-five? How did he qualify it, extending the permissible count? And how could he ignore the sign when, afterwards, a single magpie flew up from the red dogwood by the used-car forecourt?

All summer it's been building to this, the turn of the year, and what I want to forget. Dull and overripe, the clustered blackberries bulge at the edge of decomposition. Hawthorn and rowan berries are beginning to shrink; sycamore leaves shrivel at the edges, not so much changing colour as losing colour. Tortoiseshell butterflies have begun to explore the cool interior of the house. I don't want them with me, or their signal of the year's end. They creep into small gaps, into the cracks in cobwebby beams, dark niches and retreats where they will hole up, but from which they emerge sometimes on a harshly bright day in winter, when the ground is glittering with a crunch of frost. I know they can't survive, but they batter at the condensation-wet window panes, wanting out into that killing light.

After two years, after three, after seven, the signs of these days around the equinox remain the same – and the regret: that I didn't go, immediately; didn't drop everything, grab my passport, drive the five hours to the airport, catch a plane, any combination of planes, fly the twenty-four hours from Heathrow or Manchester to Dubai or Hong Kong or Singapore, and from there the eight to Brisbane – so that I might have seen her; so that I might have held her; so that I might have told her.

On the way here to the city for the test, this Tuesday morning, for my annual ritual reading of the signs, I drove in slashing rain, then sun through rain, then sun breaking through to shine on the heavy cloud massed above the city – burnished dread light, a kind of apocalyptic mid-storm reprieve. The herring gulls had come inland, flashing white against the dark sky, delighting to let themselves be shunted, and then turning about into the wind as if in defiance of that element we hardly know at all – wind like the force of death or birth; wind entering you, surrounding you, embracing and throwing you, like a man who loves with rage, unable to contain the incredulity of his hurt, of his confusion, yanking you to him, and flinging you from him. Then the gulls, letting go their defiance, slipped sideways into the wind's violent embrace.

No matter what I see in them, I know that birds are sovereign, autonomous, not subject to the projections of my small needs and anxieties. The natural world is not glorious, a respite, but a matter of implacable drives. Still I read it for signs as I have always done – as I did some thirty years ago, when a cloud of tortoiseshell butterflies emerged from the patch of nettles on a late September day, the morning I was to leave with a man I hardly knew. But what was the question then? What did they signify, those butterflies? Were they the cliché of freedom that I was about to lose, or the mad dash towards hopelessness that the frost would bring them in two days? Ten years later, sitting on the top step of the stairs to the basement, wondering how I was going to explain my injury if I went to A&E, realising that it would have to heal itself, as I would have to heal the rift again, I remembered that day watching from the upstairs window as the tortoiseshells emerged from the patch of nettle, and I thought I'd known even then the sign that they'd been giving me.

Because of the bird in the house yesterday, I have driven down for the test this morning in fear. I know what a bird in the house means. Determined, warding off bad news, I discount the solitary magpie clattering into an ash-tree, and her ominous message. Determined, I allow the black and white respite of the pair, a mile further on, flying unevenly away over a stubble field, to erase the sign she gave me. I tell myself that there have been other birds in the house and no death occurred – and deaths occur at any moment, every moment, so why suppose it's to do with me? Nevertheless, in unguarded moments, bearing in on me is the certain knowledge that a bird in the house foretells not any death but a specific death: a death in the family. Scrabbling away from it, I lie to myself that people have always had birds in the house: wild linnets or canaries in cages; chickens scratching underfoot; an African grey parrot or a turquoise and gold macaw climbing on its perch, brought back from overseas by ship, outliving its owner. And the swallows that come in, every spring, sweeping around the open door, looking for somewhere to nest: surely they erase the meaning of the bird in the house, even though they do not inexplicably appear when all the openings to the house are shut, flailing at the window, desperate to escape – as the soul from the body at the end.

I learned at the age of ten how to hold a bird. At the ringing station on Beachy Head, caught in the mist-nets strung across the tops of the chalk cliffs, the birds hung entangled, or writhed and struggled, con-vulsed with the effort to get free, and then went still. Conserving energy, only their dark glossy eyes were alert, watching my approach. I learned how to tell the sex, ruffling with a finger the soft feathers of the vent, though I don't recall the details. I was too young but not young enough to be interested in their organs of defecation or reproduction.

I don't recall what a bird's sex looks like, though I kept cage-birds – a chattering budgie; zebra finches, coloured like clowns, red-beaked and striped, endlessly hopping and beeping like some advertisement for long-life batteries. At the commercial aviary twenty miles from home, I drifted like a lover heartsick with desire through the corridors of cages that contained doves and canaries, cockatiels and rainbow lorikeets, and screeching sulphur-crested cockatoos, which climbed up the bars using beak and feet, revealing grey knobbed tongues and scaly toes.

We loved birds, my sister and I. We saved up for our budgies and finches and brought them home in small sturdy cardboard boxes which closed crisply with a flap at one end. I sat in the back seat, buckled in and keeping as still as I could against the movement of the car, feeling the weight of the new bird shift in the box from one end to the other, hearing the tiny scratch of its claws. I loved the paraphernalia of cage-birds, too – the heavy bags of seed, brittle white eye-shapes of cuttlefish bone, the nubbed sprays of dry millet, the water bottles that slotted with a blue plastic tongue through the wires of the cage front, and snapped into place in the tight metal hoop of the clasp.

The budgies and zebra finches didn't last long. Nor did my terrapins, which slowed in the cold, green-fogged water of their uncleaned tank, and then went still. My sister had a cutthroat, a bloody-necked finch; he also died. In the aviary outside the back door the quails died, taken by rats. After the aviary was floored in wire netting, the rats tunnelled underneath and ogled the new tiny flightless quails leaping in alarm as though through fear alone they might regain the lost art of getting airborne.

For a little while, though, I was devout, changing the water every day, cleaning the cages out, but soon I drifted away into neglect, and my birds hopped back and forth from perch to perch, from perch to wire cage-front, from wire to floor to perch, never flying more than two seconds. The zebra finches compensated by nesting frantically, nesting endlessly. They built and laid and built again on top of eggs, in a pathological compulsion to reproduce, and a compulsion to end it at the same time, to smother the young before they'd even hatched – and, later, to smother their young before they were even laid. Egg-bound, the females sickened and died, one by one, and the males hopped and fluttered and beeped alone, and then they too sickened and died.

She died of course – three days after the phone call, at the autumn equinox, before I had the chance to see her, before I had a chance to talk to her. Even if I had gone straight to the airport I would not have got there in time. But I already knew the outcome, because the day after the phone-call I had got up in the morning and come downstairs in the closed house and found a wren battering against the inside of the bath-room window, trying to get out. I caught it, frantic and scrabbling, and I held it, and I took it outside, and I knew my sister was going to die.

And now, the morning before my annual test, it has happened again. It was a small sound at first, a shifting in the chimney. Then, later, I heard it in the pipe behind the woodburning stove. Somehow a bird had got in through the opening under the chimney cap, had become confused, or been injured, or had dropped down inside the pipe for shelter, or as an escape from a predator. Now it was trapped in the dark, unable to spread its wings to fly back up, unable perhaps to see light beyond the bend in the pipe. It shuffled there behind the stove, scratching with small claws.

I thought I might have to sit there all day listening to its efforts to get out, hearing the stirring of soot, its claws scraping on the metal pipe, imagining its feathers blackening, bedraggled – by degrees losing energy, losing time, losing hope. And then afterwards I would begin to smell its death.

But somehow, perhaps seeing the light through the narrow flue, it struggled out of the pipe and into the stove. It stirred up the ash, and ticked with a small beak at the tarred glass of the door. I knelt before it, supplicant, and the tiny ashy creature squatted, exhausted, wings spread, beak open, watching me. I got up and closed all the curtains and opened the back door, and then I unlatched the stove door, and the bird flung itself towards the light outside.

Now, in the waiting room, remembering that ashy beak ticking at the inside of the dark glass, I flinch from the knowledge of what it means. Nothing can erase the sign it's given me. On the way, driving to the clinic, I tried to read the other signs, looking for a pair of magpies with their oracular capacity, hoping the outcome might be joy. But it's autumn and the magpies have long since separated, and one after another they told me *sorrow, sorrow, sorrow* – that one, rising from the fox carcass; that one by the slaughterhouse, launching itself across the road; that one perched on a telegraph pole, watching me pass.

Everything else was a sign to something I could not read: the curlews stalking in the stubble; a pale fox trotting along an invisible path; a heron awkward and humped on a rusting gate, and the purple willowherb, now merely bare and drying canes.

Here in the city, the trees have begun to turn. I realise that once again it is merely days till the anniversary of my sister's death, and I think of the single magpies foretelling sorrow, and it catches me suddenly, sharp as though it happened a mere week ago, the intensity of the loss. Because the losses still accumulate, as each of our experiences together dies – like the memory of sitting beside her with the bird boxes, now fading because it is no longer shared.

In the waiting room, it is my turn: the beech veneer door opens, and the nurse calls my name. I go through and hear the door close heavily behind me as I prepare for the indignity of having my breasts lifted and draped and pulled and then squashed flat as though they are accidental appendages that hardly belong to me.

My sister's death has increased my risk, so each year in the autumn near the anniversary of her death I face not the possibility but the certainty of my own mortality, as every woman in that waiting room does. Every woman preparing herself, baring herself, submitting to the machinery, is facing what my sister was too afraid to face: that the reading of the signs might tell her what she knew was true.

I never told her about my own fear, because I too did not recognise it as fear: it was an element I lived in, like the gulls in the wind. I navigated its swell, its ebb and flow, reading its signs, waiting for it to peak and subside. I have never since known an intimacy like that. *It will be OK*, I told myself, the last time, sitting at the top of the stairway down to the basement. On my shoulder, whispering in my ear, there was a small hawk, telling me *repair repair repair*. It was a sparrowhawk, hooded, belled, like something out of TH White. I was suspended from my life, knowing that if I just did the right thing, if I read the signs correctly, if

I interpreted the signs he was giving me, it would be OK: I'd be safe, for a bit. The sparrowhawk was like the disembodied voice of my pathology. And that time, the last time, for a short while the knowledge of choice was intoxicating. I knew what I had to do; I knew if I did it, the reward would be great. I could choose to mend the breach. I always could choose that. I always had mended the breach. If I gave him a way out, apologised, said it was my fault, everything would be repaired, and I would be safe again, for a while.

There is nothing like the naked intimacy of violence, when all that you fear is realised, and all pretence has been blown aside. And when you have taken the blame, abased yourself, crept on your belly like a muddied, bedraggled fox at bay, and the master of hounds has whipped off his dogs – for he is always both hunter and saviour – there is nothing like the intimacy of reconciliation after violence. When fear lifts, when you have asked for redemption, and he has given you redemption, you could not be closer, you could never feel more full of trust – for he is stunned by his capacity to lose control, appalled that it has happened; he is solicitous and tender, and full of regret. No one can know what the two of you know. You can't share with anyone but one another this trust, the unbreakable intimacy of this secret, this shared culpability, and the heady, light relief when you are, for those few moments – minutes, maybe half a day or a day, until it begins to fall away again – safe.

By the time I come out of the clinic the storm has blown inland, and the gulls have returned to the shore. Rooks and jackdaws are turning on their backs in the wind above the dirty farm where the three-legged dog always leaps barking at my front wheels. Full of dread, I am for one moment reprieved by a pair of magpies, and my heart leaps up with the terrified optimism of the quails in the aviary.

While I wait for the test results that long fortnight as the year shifts towards winter, the autumn becomes rot and chaos. The kite turning above something that has drowned in the torrential rain means nothing more than its own hunger. The hawthorn, heavy with berries the colour of old blood, points to earlier weather conditions, not to the weather conditions I project – the hard winter that never comes. The real story that the dying world is telling is a story of eating and shitting, of rutting and birthing, of threat and fear, of dying and rotting and beginning again, and, after the cycle ends, the compulsion to go on.

When at last the letter arrives, telling me of my reprieve, as it does each year for another year, my sister's death is behind me, my own mortality is at bay, and suddenly, released from the grip of fear, I am alive, sharply alive – as I was after violence, after everything nameless and bulging was made real. How exquisitely he could love me then. And how exquisitely I too could love in that temporary, heady release from the clamp of fear.

I think of the man in the waiting room, weeping behind his newspaper, as the woman he loved was submitting to the investigation of her body, and I feel for him a kind of tender longing, wondering if I can ever have a love like theirs. Because I know, now, that those dark eyes, that small beak ticking at the window of the stove, that unrecognisable ashy bird, was not looking out of its own life, or out of its own cage, but into mine.

Jasmine Donahaye won the New Welsh Writing Awards 2021 Rheidol Prize for Prose with a Welsh Theme or Setting with her essay collection 'Reading the Signs' (to be published on our Rarebyte book imprint), from which this is an extract. Her previous publications include narrative nonfiction, fiction, poetry and cultural criticism. Her memoir, *Losing Israel* (2015), won the nonfiction category of Wales Book of the Year, and her story, 'Theft', was shortlisted for the Royal Society of Literature's VS Pritchett Memorial Prize in 2016. Her books include a biography of Lily Tobias, *The Greatest Need* (2015); a cultural study, *Whose People? Wales, Israel, Palestine* (2012) and two poetry collections, *Self-Portrait as Ruth* (2009), which was longlisted for Wales Book of the Year, and *Misappropriations* (2006), which was shortlisted for the Jerwood Aldeburgh First Collection Prize. Her work has appeared in literary journals, and in the *New York Times* and *The Guardian*. She was elected a Fellow of the Learned Society of Wales in 2017.

THE REBECCAS

NOVELLA EXTRACT BY **JACK HARRIS**

And they blessed Rebekah, and said to her, You are our sister, be you the mother of thousands of millions, and let your seed possess the gate of those which hate them.

THAT WAS ONE EXPLANATION FOR IT. THE LINES WERE FROM GENESIS, 24:6. Another was, that when the men realised none of their wives' clothes would fit them, they'd gone to see a stout old matriarch known as Big Rebecca and helped themselves to her dresses.

Any excuse, like! said a boy at the back of the classroom, and then another boy, lacking the satire of his friend, perhaps hoping to compensate with sheer brevity, just said, Gays!

For years, Sean had favoured the Biblical origin, it's solemnity so commensurate with the task at hand. The gate was right on the money, a very neat touch, and he liked to think those guys knew what they were doing. Having been back in the town the best part of a year now, he was starting to think again. This was not the shock of the new, but the shock of the old and put aside, the musk of the reluctantly dusted-off.

Just then, he was standing in front of his Year Eights. After lunch break, the trick was to let them get the sugar out of their systems, proceeding through bursts of clamour and sass until their energy was gone and they settled. After that, they just sat in front of him, taciturn as slate heaps. Still, he was trying to get them interested, trying to show them why this stuff was important.

He singled out a girl on the front table, a Carys or a Cerys, he couldn't remember which. Let's try this, he said, and then asked her what her dad did.

Builder, sir.

He already knew this, had picked her out because of it. He was no good with their names, even this far into his career, but he knew their points of origin. She was Staf Richards' girl, the youngest of three.

Builder, great. What does he need to be a builder?

Dunno, sir. What do you mean, sir?

What did she mean *what do you mean, sir?* Still, he persevered.

What I mean is, when he goes to work in the morning, what does he take with him? What does he need to buy?

This was better. The Richards girl took the bait, reeling off a line of essential supplies: spades, shovels, cement, bricks, nails, screws.

From somewhere else in the classroom, another voice took up the slack. Same, sir. My dad's a builder, too.

Over the next five minutes, Sean established what all of their mums and dads did for work and what it took to keep them doing it. He asked them how they liked weekends and holidays. What about when Mum was sick, did that mean she'd have to go without pay for a week? It turned out Kerry Evans had an older brother on Universal Credit. He was pretty useless, like, but did he deserve to starve?

He was encouraged. They were coming along with him, if not entirely enthusiastic, then at least animated. The stream was dug, but the river was still a way off. This bit was always the trickiest. There was a leap required, a slight shift of focus which nonetheless retained a view of the present object. Where, he asked them at once, did all those things come from? How would Carys' dad feel – Cerys, sorry – if the price of cement went up, or if Jewson's started charging him for parking?

And there the stream ran dry. He had failed again. A whole half term on this, and apparently there was no way to reconcile the two pictures, to show how their own lives leaned back on the cost of lime in the nineteenth century, the road tolls suffered by their distant antecedents. By the time he got to the dresses, it was all too strange, too much like something that happened ages ago and didn't happen any more. Wearily, he conceded.

OK. Open your textbooks and read pages twenty to twenty-three.

He was telling Dom about it at The Lamb later, three Stellas in, circling a pool table.

The old textbook save, then?

That's the one.

Shame there's no sandpit.

I'd not put it past them.

A stray yellow banked off the cushion and disappeared into a corner pocket. It was not the shot's intended target, but a happy piece of collateral damage.

Dom tapped two fingers on the table in acknowledgement. Your problem is you're a fucking poet. Everything has to fit.

His friend looked up at him from the vertex of a pool cue. It wasn't the first time he'd made that point, but still it rang out, a gong of insight. His follow-up shot was surer, a back-spun drill into the corner pocket. The yellow sank and the white reversed, aligning with its next mark.

My problem is *I* don't fit. These are the same kids who thought I was weird back then.

Bollocks. They were alright on Saturday. We had a good night, didn't we?

They had done, but as always there were concessions. Sean had gone over late afternoon and met them in the Drovers' beer garden. Some of them still had their cricket whites on, fragrant and flecked with mud. A few were young and unfamiliar to him, but there were a couple he remembered from school, softer now and tired, sitting beside the gently swollen versions of themselves who were their fathers. He'd got a round in to show willing then perched beside them on the canopied picnic bench and waited.

As always, Dom had provided him with an opening. Look at this boy, though. The only person I know who can fall *up*stairs!

They'd looked over at him and laughed. That was harmless enough on the first dose.

Sean wasn't a bad sport. He'd laughed too, playing along.

How'd you manage that then?

Oh God, that's not even all of it. One time when we lived together.... Dom hadn't been trying to get one up on him. His was the flag they all rallied round, a bit of boozy heraldry, all lions and tankards. Sean's colours were less clear to them. It wasn't enough that he could match them all pint for pint or go in just as hard on the dirty stuff, but it wasn't that any more was required of him, either. However willingly Sean inhabited that world it wasn't his to inhabit. What they needed from him was less, and so he swapped his odd banner for a plain, white sheet, and waited while Dom told the beer can story.

They were living in London at the time. Dom was working at a local gym, trying to drum up clients for personal training. Sean was trying to write, trying to publish, but really not doing much of anything. Their flat belonged to Dom's step-mother, who'd grown up there in the sixties. There was an extra bedroom and a proper lounge opening onto a balcony with a view of the estate, a ring of sturdy maisonettes flanked by larches. The balcony was where they went in the evenings to drink cheap lager and review the incidents of the day. The rent was decent, and even though the boys eventually found their respective disappointments heavy enough to send each of them home, they were lucky to have the place then, that year. It was a strong moment while it was theirs, charged with the rhythms of newness.

One summer evening, they spilled out from the balcony into a couple of the local bars, then took a bus to the bridge. The riverside pubs all had their colours on and there was light on the water where the sun had come to rest, leaving its perfume in the hanging baskets. After closing time they'd bought a few cans from a nearby offy and stomped up and down the north bank, singing and crying. It was a night of no real event, but in their shared memory it smouldered.

Sean woke early the next morning and made straight for the bathroom. Suppressing a spasm of vomit, he pissed hard into the bowl, then took a swig of cold water from the tap. Focussing on the mirror until his reflections had gathered, he noted he was in his pyjamas, which was a victory of sorts. Still, it was no good going back to bed, he was up now, jolted into being. Putting on his dressing gown, he went out onto the balcony. The detritus of the night before lay about him, probably twelve or thirteen cans.

…So then he thinks he'd better make a start on the recycling. Right then, like. Probably six o'clock. I wake up hanging out my arsehole and there's this huge noise going on.

Sean had got the rubbish through to the kitchen, and then he remembered something from primary school, the visit of the recycling lady, who had told them all it was much better to crush cans with your feet before disposing of them. He couldn't remember why that was, but he could see the kids she'd called up to have a go at it, each growing less and less tentative until all the teachers buckled.

…I come into the kitchen and he's there in a dressing gown and brogues and I'm like what the fuck's going on and he looks at me and says –

Dom always delivered the punchline the same way, a flat, dopey monotone, the sort of voice you'd hear coming out of a cartoon bear –

CRUSHING CANS!

Though most of them had heard it before, the table shook with delight.

Crushing cans! Like it was the most normal thing in the world! Christ. I'll never forget.

A good sport. He definitely was one. By now the story was perennial, but even on this airing, Sean laughed along, offering the same numbskull responses – Well, you know, seemed like the thing to do at the time.

Dom sat back happily, satisfied that he'd made his friend a place at the table. The piss he took out of him was the same piss he took out of the boys, which in turn was the same piss they took out of Dom and the same piss they took out of Sean. It wasn't, though, that was the trouble. It really wasn't.

Better get them in, then.

Dom had made the most of his advantage, parlaying the run of yellows into a single black, dropped neatly in a centre pocket. Sean went to the bar and got two more Stellas.

I've only got a twenty. Is that okay?

That's fine. We tend to draw the line at fifty, like.

A group of sixth-formers had entered the other side of the pub. One boy was bare-chested, covered in paint and streamers. Others wore clashing pringle vests and comedy golf clothes, bearing inflatable putters. They were building a line of sambucas across the bar. Sean covered his face and ducked back to the corner nook Dom had claimed.

Neck this quick. We'll go somewhere else.

Dom obliged and the two of them grabbed their jackets and made for the back door. The boys, meanwhile, had seen away the sticky black shots and made it to the pool table, stacking a pile of coins on the cushion. One of them was wearing a silver sequinned dress and suspenders with fishnets. A bright yellow wig spread out under his plastic cowboy hat. Sean thought of his Year Eights, still a few years off the pubs. They'd be out there now, nervously sending the largest among them into Tesco's for cans of their own. Then he looked back at the lad in the silver dress, a helium balloon saying '17' tied to his shoulder strap.

Any excuse, like, he thought.

Jack Harris was born in Builth Wells, Powys, and studied English at Oxford. He currently lives in Hackney, East London.

FESTIVAL
OF THE GHOST

NOVELLA EXTRACT BY **JOAO MORAIS**

27 March, 1.50pm

I READ SOMEWHERE THAT KEEPING A JOURNAL CAN HELP WITH THE GRIEVING process. Every time I have a thought about you, or something happens that reminds me of you, I'm supposed to write it down.

Well, today was meant to be the day of our final goodbye, so you were always going to be the only thing on my mind.

It was just you and me left in the hall. But I couldn't even, for the very last time, see your face and kiss you on the cheek. My silence was broken by a long unpunctuated message I received from whom I assumed was the lorry driver. I stared at a ceiling light, like I always have to, when I want to feel clean, doing what you and Mum used to call one of my funny little quirks.

But your casket wasn't even in a straight line. I needed the release, I needed to find its correct position. If I didn't, then I couldn't be clean again.

I wheeled you until your casket was parallel with the back window. But then the flowers on top weren't in balance with the lectern, so I rearranged them to make sure the pinks and purples didn't touch. I looked down and I found myself clicking my fingers, trying to find the right pattern which would stop me feeling like there was a tumour growing in my head.

And in that second I noticed I was no longer alone.

It was you.

I don't know how but you were stood at the lectern. You were dressed in black and your hair was up and your mouth was moving as if you were talking, but no sound came out. Then you stopped, and stared at the back of the hall.

I fell into a seat. You were in the casket. I had helped carry you in myself. The violence of what had happened to you was in there. But you looked so young. You were skinnier and smaller, somehow, with a rounder face.

And I knew, right then, that I had seen you like this before.

Five years ago at Mum's funeral. You caught me sneaking in late and I had to stand at the back. You'd spotted me and welled up and you couldn't get your words out. And now I was seeing you go through it again.

And just like that you were gone.

I grabbed at the air where I'd seen you. I looked at the casket, at the flowers on top. I went to look inside, but the thought of what I would see made me cold and weak.

Outside there was a sea of people in black. I walked through the mulls and murmurs. A man with a big collar said sorry for my loss. The undertaker, Mr Sparrow – the same one we had for Mum – asked if I was ready to head to the wake.

But all I could say was, – I saw her. I just saw Alexis in the hall.

And all he could say back was, – I'm not sure you should tell anyone that at the wake, son.

I pushed past one of your friends in a yellow coat and went back in. The lectern was in the same place, but now it didn't look like it was aligned correctly with the wall, as if its position made the whole world wrong.

I shifted it over. But this made me feel like my body was open to disease, so I started to brush down the parts that felt open, and at the lectern I saw a woman crying. She was wearing a bonnet and a man came up to her holding a handkerchief and he was bald, but he'd combed his hair over, and then they disappeared.

I heard the doors go and the undertakers came through. Mr Sparrow said, – The next mourners need to prepare now, son.

They were walking up the aisle. I said, – I saw her at the lectern, and then I saw a woman and a man.

I didn't even believe it myself. But I knew I had seen all this with my own eyes.

Mr Sparrow said, after a second, – It's been a stressful day for you. I tell you, son, what will help is if you get a drink down you at the wake. Talk about her. Let other people tell you about her.

He moved his hand slowly and put it round my elbow.

– I'll show you what I mean, I said.

I went up to the lectern and tried to adjust it, but I didn't feel anything. It was just a lectern in a hall in front of your dead body.

Mr Sparrow said, – We have to be fair on the next mourners, sir.

I ignored him. I started moving the lectern around but nothing happened. I did some of my finger-strumming rituals that you used to find funny when we were kids, even though I didn't feel the need to do them. But nothing was happening.

I followed Mr Sparrow down the aisle and I heard a younger undertaker whisper, – What is it with this guy and funerals?

Mr Sparrow told him to be quiet.

I shook the hands of a hundred people, all offering their condolences and offering to buy me a drink at the wake.

But I wasn't listening.

All I could think about was you.

6pm

At The Steamboat, Aunty kept on trying to get our little cousins to come over to me in the corner. But they could see that I didn't want to talk. I pretended to go to the toilet and left through the beer garden.

An envelope was half hanging out of our letterbox. I pushed it in with my knuckle, careful to only use the middle one so I didn't feel unclean. A woman walked through our front door as if it wasn't there.

She was big, and her skin looked as if she had spent most of her life under the faraway sun, and not the clouds of the dockland sky. She was wearing a blue apron and a scarf of yellow around her head, and she walked straight past me and she was gone.

I just wanted it to stop.

I wanted to feel clean again.

I let myself in. One of your boxes on the sofa had some papers peeping out the side. I had to sort them, to make sure they were all straight and in a line. I took them and jabbed them tidy on the floor, then stacked them back in the box.

And I saw you.

This time you were looking out the window. You were wearing that dark blue hoodie you never gave me back.

You shut the curtain and disappeared.

I nudged the box again, but nothing happened. It felt like it was where it was supposed to be. I tried once more but I knew I was wasting my time.

Then I heard the front door. I walked out of the living room and there was a man dressed in black, stood by the stairs. I vaguely recalled him waiting in line to shake my hand, because he had a big collar.

I didn't want another person asking if they could do anything to help. So I said, – You know, it's rude to just walk into people's houses.

And he said, – Didn't you hear me calling?

– This is kind of a shit day for me.

– I didn't mean to barge in. I didn't know how else to get your attention, sorry. My name is Ted Hurley. Your sister was my doctoral student.

When you got accepted, I remember you telling me how excited you were by your new supervisor. He was why you chose your home town over Bristol in the first place.

I said, – Alexis told me about you. Didn't you go out of your way to help her get that bursary?

He said, – I guess so. Anyway, I'm sorry to bother you at this time. It's just that what I wanted to ask is better coming from me in person. I was wondering if you knew what she did with her thesis?

– Why do you need that? I said.

– She only uploaded certain chapters to her student records. But I know she was very close to submitting, and I feel that if I handed it in with a strong letter of recommendation, her doctorate could be awarded posthumously.

I couldn't explain how I regretted it now, how when we went to Aunty's birthday we ended up ignoring each other. So I said, – I don't know anything about it, to be honest. We fell out a few weeks ago.

Here is something I will never get the chance to say. Do you remember, when we last spoke, how you said I was smothering you after I accused you of being really distant lately? It wasn't you who was being the dickhead.

He said, after a moment or so, – Do you have any of her study stuff here? I mean I know it's not ideal, but if I could take it off you now I could submit it by the end of the academic year.

We went into the living room. I pointed at your boxes and turned to the window. I opened the curtains to give him more light, but I couldn't stop tugging the one on the left, even though it was fully back. And then I got the urge to stub my toe and out of nowhere I saw four men at a table playing cards.

Two of them were black and one white and one from the Middle East, but they didn't have any feet, their ankles in the ground. They were not quite there, as if I was looking at their reflections in a pane of glass. They were smoking and one of them laughed, and then they were gone.

I looked at Hurley. In the end, he said, – I'm not sure what I saw there.

– I'm more glad that it's not just in my head, I said.

Then he looked at me straight and said, – It's not just in your head. I don't know how else to say this, but you've worked out how to loop.

6.20pm

He said, – I can't explain what I mean without showing you.

So I said, – Then show me.

When I shut the front door, I squeezed the handle until my hand cramped. Now I could tell myself that the pain meant I didn't have to go back and check it was locked.

Hurley was waiting for me by the gate. – Took you a while to close the door, he said.

– I like to double check.

– You mean you had to perform a ritual.

He turned and walked. He would only know this if he did the same thing.

We went past a bunch of boys listening to some tinny grime on a phone, and made our way through the maze of the estate where the cars can't go.

Hurley said, – What do you know of the history of this place?

– Not as much as my sister.

We joined the road and got to Callaghan Square, the one with the tall glass banks and the fountain. He said, – OK then. Any idea what was here before this corporate monstrosity?

And I said, – This was all a building site when I was a kid.

– It was the Greek part of the city, he said. – Right next to the Somali quarter. Sailors brought their families over and settled in the streets where this square now is. They came from all over the world, and other sailors would meet Welsh women here and get married and make this their home port.

He looked around, then took off his shoe and lined it up so that it was perpendicular to the fountain.

The type of look he had on his face, I had felt on my own. He had to get it right. It had to be perfect or it would leave him unclean. Then he took out some keys and arranged them until they were in a star shape and put them on the floor.

There were little kids playing in the fountain. Two brown boys wearing shorts and shoes and three white girls in long dresses. The girl in front turned around and she was smiling and running and then they were gone.

He put his shoe back on as I asked him what the fuck, but he walked off and I had to run to catch up. I asked him again, but there were some men waiting to be let inside the Salvation Army.

When I told him to slow down he stopped and picked up a couple of stones from the gutter. He put a few of them in a triangle and twisted his ear and I saw a bunch of black men in the road. One was rolling up a sleeve and two others were watching another man check how many bullets he had in a gun.

– I always feel bad for these guys, Hurley said. – A big crowd of demobbed Kiwi soldiers has barricaded them inside their lodgings. All for the crime of having jobs and being black.

And I said, – But that's not possible. That's the race riots of 1919.

He looked at me and said, – That's what it is, though. We're seeing ghosts. These are the animations of past lives. When people experience a moment of high emotion, like joy or love or stress, an imprint gets stored where it happened. Events of the past are all around us, and if you can bring about just the right conditions, they can be released for all the world to see.

I sat on the kerb. He sat down next to me and I said, – This is a lot to take in.

– It gets quite cool after a while, he said. – I've seen Henry VIII with half his nose lost to syphilis. One of the few who've seen Caesar greeting Cleopatra for the first time at the gates of Rome.

I said, – One of the few?

– Let's just say we're not the only ones.

I thought about what it could mean. I didn't really care to see old kings and queens. If Hurley could see them, however, then maybe I could see Mum and you.

I said, – I think I wanna give it another try.

We walked back towards the dock, past the Lagos cafe and the turning for the mosque.

Hurley stopped and said, – There's one here. You'll learn that. Look at that kerb jutting out.

It looked like any other. A car went past. I felt nothing.

He sighed and kicked a cigarette packet from the gutter and scratched his left knee.

Out of nowhere, a pretty young woman in a bonnet was looking at me. She was sat down at a table and she smiled. But this smile felt like it was for me. It was as if our eyes connected. The feeling of unease it gave me was enough to put a chill up my spine.

When she disappeared, I said, – I swear she could see me.

– Don't forget that it's an animation, Hurley said. – She's in a dock-side cafe, trying to catch a sailor's eye so he would go in and give her business. She was rather famous, actually.

– What was her name?

– Mary Jane Kelly.

I shrugged and said nothing.

– Maybe you haven't heard of Mary Jane Kelly. But I bet you've heard of the man who killed her.

There was only one person he could mean. Everyone knew the stories. So I said, – I guess she must have been one of the Butcher of Butetown's victims.

– The Butcher never actually killed in Butetown, you know. He did them all in other parts of the city. That was just the racism of the time. People back then believed that the murders couldn't have been done by someone of good Welsh stock, they must have been done by a foreigner. Mary Jane Kelly, this poor young girl, maybe spooked by the reports of the Butcher in the papers, left for London. Then a couple of years later, on a wet, cold night in November 1888, this unlucky girl became the final known victim of Jack the Ripper.

I said nothing.

– Now you try, he said.

I smoothed down my arms. I picked up the cigarette packet and dropped it on its side. And then you appeared in front of us. You were hopping on one foot and bending down and then you disappeared.

For a long moment, we were silent.

And then Hurley said, – I wish she'd told me.

João Morais came second in the New Welsh Writing Awards (NWWA) 2021 Rheidol Prize for Prose with a Welsh Theme or Setting with 'Festival of the Ghost', extracted here. He recently completed a PhD in Creative Writing at Cardiff University. He was previously longlisted for the NWWA Americymru Prize for the Novella, shortlisted for the Academi Rhys Davies Short Story Prize, the Percy French Prize for Comic Verse, and the All Wales Comic Verse Award. He won the 2013 Terry Hetherington Prize for Young Writers. His short story collection, *Things That Make the Heart Beat Faster*, is published by Parthian.

THANK YOU TO OUR #SECURENEWWELSHREVIEW SUPPORTERS

Diamond Supporters:
Mary Chadwick
Professor Tony Curtis
Mary Oliver
Kaite O'Reilly

Platinum Supporters:
Tasha Alden
Ruhi Behi
E Clifford Cutler
Jasmine Donahaye
Elaine Ewart
Katie Gramich

Kurt Heinzelman
Gareth Lewis
Rhiannon Lewis
Susan Merriman
Jackie Morris
Dr Chris W Pitt
Jim Pratt
Tracey Rhys
Amy Strange
Clive Upton
Roger Williams
Carole Hailey

THE KAISER AND THE RIVER

STORY BY **SYBILLA HARVEY**

EACH TUESDAY, I WOULD WALK TO THE RIVER. I USED TO SWIM THERE AS a child before it was called wild swimming, drank there when I was too young for the pubs and got down on my hands and knees and cried out of boredom, which often turned to exhilaration, such was the water's effect. During the last year of the war, I just looked at the river and watched how simple it was for one thing to keep moving despite being filled with death. There was definitely some comfort to be had in seeing the water rush over a drowned and bloated fox caught on a fallen branch. And I have continued to find comfort there. My life runs as far as the river's bend. I have lived in houses with sullen stone fronts on both sides of town, but never beyond the curve where the river turns and heads out to the estuary.

I couldn't tell you why I chose to walk there on Tuesdays, but it was probably because my younger brother Ben was in the late days of his sickness. I wanted to be anywhere but the hospital. It was already full of soldiers with black shadows around their eyes, men who were taken out to our countryside to heal. It also contained my brother and his unhealing. Tuesdays were when Ben had his most serious treatments. His cells are under attack, the doctor told us, as if likening his situation to that of the country made it easier to understand. Ben was thirteen, wore thick glasses and kept an inhaler in his back pocket at all times, which he did sometimes pull out and puff at me like a gun, the air turning metallic.

I had a job share at the time with a woman called Bill. I was too young to join the Land Army and Bill had allergies so couldn't go to the farms, but I think she just didn't want to. I did mornings in the office, she did afternoons. We called it the office when really it was an empty changing room for the retired town swimming pool and sports hall, now occupied by the army. We would receive the messages from London and run them over to the officers in the hall next door, who would clap us as we ran towards them like horses they had a bet on. The pool was drained and when no one was about I would climb down into it and pretend I was on the seabed like a sunken battleship. Sometimes, I stood on the blue tiles and stretched my arms out like I was a beautiful figurehead guiding us all to a better place. A few months after Ben died, she took me on the train to Cardiff so she could buy me drinks on Queen Street and I could forget it all. She drank so much she lay on the paving stones and looked up at the sky until the sun disappeared. There it is, there it is, there it is, it's gone, she said. She was a modern woman for the time.

The afternoon light on the riverbank was sometimes bright but mostly grey, which I never minded. My bench was halfway along the water, and I walked to it in all weathers, even snow, when the river's surface looked the way gravy does when fat rises to the top. I'd walk down the path from the town castle that overlooked the water and into the meadows and straight to my bench. It had a plaque saying: 'Kay Rees loved it here.' And so did I. Back then, if one person was sitting on it, I didn't mind sharing; if a few people were spread out across the hard wooden seat, I purposefully stood too close to them, skimming stones and humming until they moved.

The first time I saw him was in early summer. I wore a red cotton sundress and white tennis shoes, which were never used for tennis. They're still at the back of my wardrobe, scuffed with a rich green from my afternoon walks. I marvel at how narrow my feet were, like lovely piano keys. I had flying saucers in my pocket. The visiting GI had given them to me as a present before he was sent home; I felt myself hug him with glee before I realised what I was doing and it was as if his heart was not a heart but an angry cuckoo trying to mine its way out. Mam didn't eat much when Ben was ill, which made the rationing easier, but I still dreamt of sugar the way a child does. I was sixteen that month, and some men looked at me like I was still a child, but others didn't. This GI didn't. I could feel my body running in front of me and I wasn't quite ready to catch it up; I was shocked and seduced by how much older I looked, what I was capable of. I think the first time the man on the bench saw me, I had my fingers in my mouth, licking that sherbet off. I never usually asked if I could sit down but this time I did; something about his posture made me: he was as upright as an oak. He just nodded.

The bench made its usual creak as I readjusted myself and placed my hands in my lap, turning the ring on my little finger. He wore no jewellery, not even a watch. His blue sports jacket was flannel soft and matched his trousers. He had a medicinal smell mixed with sweat, and his suede slippers reminded me of a toddler's booties. I remember how his breathing was in time with the sway of the trees. I ate another flying saucer, biting around its papery edges and taking the lid off, dipping my tongue into the crystals. His eagle's brow caught my eye: long, dark and feathery. His jaw was Ken-doll square. He reminded me of those terriers that look like old men. I still find myself not being content with a thing just as it is. It has to be something more, has to look like something else. My husband says it's an affliction of living through the war: to see something as it truly is can be unbearable. I swallowed the rest of the flying saucer and did what I always did: looked out at the river and waited for the day to pass. Can I have one, he asked.

In the evenings, I helped out at the Labour club, opening beer bottles we kept in buckets of cold water. It was the same small crowd most nights who kept close to the bar so that the rest of the old hall looked empty. We played no music and, when one of them laughed, it echoed and I felt it in my teeth. You saw it all, over the course of a shift: town life reflected in the Formica surfaces, tears dripping on beer mats, fights. When others started to come home from the war, and some didn't, the club filled up with all sorts of emotions which sloshed about and men began asking me if I had a boyfriend. I took to pinching my cheeks in the bathroom so that I looked flushed and pretty. Those cheeks are like berries, they said. I was too young to know what the war did to people then but I can say that standing in the Labour club that summer was like being in a jar of cotton wool, as if those men inside the club were too sharp and in too many pieces to be out on their own. When our neighbour, whose son hadn't come home, walked in and asked me how Mam was coping with Ben being in hospital, I dropped a glass. No one had said it out loud before. The smash made one man fall to the floor and cover his ears. Get down, he shouted, and I crouched down too, to make him feel less ashamed about it all. On the floor, I thought of my brother's face, how it was like a moon.

I went back to the river the following Tuesday, and this time he was on my side of the bench, wearing the same outfit, same posture. I noticed a tag around his wrist which I'd missed the previous week. I said hello and he said it back. His German accent was a glitch; I knew not to trust it, not to like it, and the hairs on my arms announced themselves. Yet he was there and sitting quietly before the river and not trying to kill me. I chose to ignore it like so many things we don't question or acknowledge when we're young, like how our mams never smiled or how they looked sixty-six when they were actually thirty-six. The swans were out that day and when I think of our second meeting, they float across my mind, beautiful white sculptures snaking around him. I had a new mix of sweets in my pocket, the full eight ounces, and I could tell he wanted one; he swallowed awkwardly because his mouth was watering so much. His cheeks seemed to have sunk in a week and his eyes were heavy. I hadn't noticed how thin he was the first time we sat together; his knees were like the sharpest rocks on the riverbank. I decided I would not give him a sweet until I knew more about him, and even then, I wasn't sure I wanted to share.

He was staying at the Court and it took me a while to work out which one he meant. I immediately pictured the court we'd all go to in my last year of school. It was infamous to those of us who'd known it. Around the back of our assembly hall, the dead grass stretched out alongside a corrugated bomb shelter we called the Worm. After the final bell went one day and lessons were done, some of us gathered in the court to kiss, while others leant against the cool iron of the shelter and smoked. The head girl gave five hand jobs to four boys one after the other while we all watched. I think of that boldness now as heroic; we found a way to do a lot with not much at all. We cheered her on and I remember how her tights became loose around the ankles with the effort; how a film of sweat broke out across her top lip. I remember how the boys closed their eyes, their own private blackouts. A teacher caught us and cried. Her face reminded me of the crisp packets Ben and I put in the oven when we had nothing else to do. The way they shrank and cowered.

The man on the bench was not at that court but the place my mam was almost admitted to after Ben died. They did not usually let the patients roam; they stayed inside the old Edwardian pile on the edge of town eating custard and other soft things to line their stomachs against the pills they swallowed. We heard stories about the electric shocks that ran through people's bodies; I imagined it like having a tuning fork placed inside you. I have my own lodgings there, he told me, as he put a lemon sherbet in his mouth. Just until they work out what to do with me, he said. The sourness did not bother him; he crunched on the drop of yellow sugar and asked for another as soon as it had gone. I found myself saying yes; there was something about his wanting. Where are you from, he asked, and I pointed behind me towards the greening copper of the town hall roof, past the meadows and the castle. We lived on the few floors above the chip shop. I thought that maybe I shouldn't have even pointed in the direction of our house; patients from the Court often escaped and knocked on doors asking to be taken home. His was a strange freedom. I learned he was allowed to walk out when he wanted; he climbed the Skirrid mountain most mornings, even walked to the local pub to drink a wine. I'm enjoying this sight, he said, and ran his hand along the river as if she were a woman performing a striptease just for him. The current was fast that day and the water jumped over the boulders in its way, frothing at the edges.

Over the years, many have come here to hide or be hidden, to disappear in the hills around us, the quiet roads shadowed by trees, a green little town where not much happens. Our town name translates as mouth of the river; it's the beginning of something, the start of a race where we're all waiting for a gun to go off so we can start running. Not long ago, and a long time since I shared my sweets with the man on the bench, there was word a woman who helped kill two children was released from prison and placed here while her new identity was formed, like a jelly you put in the fridge to set. She had a face like no other and soon people began to talk. I thought I saw her handling an onion in the grocers. I felt my face go the colour of its papery pink shell and put my basket down and left. More people talked and the journalists turned up on the high street, trying to catch a glimpse of her. It was said she was rehomed after that. Sometimes, I don't know whether to be offended by it: that people believe you can disappear here, that nature's wildness can absorb your own. What does it mean for those of us who already choose to be in this town surrounded by mountains? Just because I am out of the way does not mean I haven't spent my life trying to be seen.

Ben would not mind me blaming him. I did not know who the man on the bench was. Even when I wasn't thinking about my brother, he was there, as if he had set up his tent in my mind's eye. Before he got ill, he used to go camping deep into the Beacons with his friends for long weekends, his skinny arms swinging by his sides, an extra inhaler in his rucksack. Even though he's been gone much longer than he was alive, he is still pitching up next to my half-formed thoughts, my to-buy lists, the friends' birthdays I should have remembered. The war was ending but I barely looked at a newspaper. Mam took to eating blancmange because she said it went down easier and she had the coupons for it. On those days, she let me get pie and chips from the shop below. I saw the newspapers; they were used to wrap the chips but I was only interested in the grease and the salt and vinegar and the way the flavours flooded my mouth, in the same way I liked to feel the river rush over my feet when I stood in it. I missed the headline about the Nazi on the bench crashing his plane in Scotland, making a break from Germany. I bit into the lard-grey crust of the pie and thought about my brother and only my brother. I thought about his pills as big as mint imperials; how I had tried to joke that radiotherapy was like the doctors using the wireless to put a song through his body. When he drank a can of pop, he never pulled the ring back completely. I missed the headline that the Nazi on the bench had been captured in Scotland and taken away somewhere.

Somewhere. Around the fourth or fifth time I saw him, I pulled out my almost empty bag of sweets and put a barley twist in my mouth and gave one to him. My hair was wet from dunking my head in the sink at the office so I must have dripped on him when I sat on the bench. Why don't you swim in there, he asked me, the boiled sweet on his tongue making his words thick. I told him I do, but not today. I've heard there are waterfalls around here, he said. There were, there are. We took my daughter there when she was young and she would jump into the freezing pools again and again. Women in my family are a magnet for the good sort of pain, for getting their bodies out. It's too far to walk, I told the man on the bench. Perhaps they'll drive me before I go, he said, looking at my legs. I crossed them so that my skirt rose higher. His stomach growled, a wet gurgling thing, like the puddles around us that had appeared after the night's rain.

In the sixties, I met my husband next to a burger van. I laughed at the logo: a cow wearing a chef's hat, and he turned around to look at me with his bacon bap. It had taken me a while to find someone I liked. It amazes us daily that we are still alive and believe it's because we have done life's portions just right. We didn't rush to meet each other or treat love like it was the last panicked hour before the shops close. We took our time and, because of that, were given more in return. We meditated on love, like the ancient monk on Cross Street. He sits outside Greggs, impossibly alive in his orange robes, cross-legged on the ground like a jewel someone dropped.

The day we met, there was a demonstration in town for those who were killed in the accident at the colliery and we found ourselves following it, using protest as an excuse to keep talking, the faces of the dead men bobbing above us on home-made signs. I thought of them as handsome finger puppets. I'm going to his funeral next week, my husband said, pointing to one of the miners. I did not tell him then that the only funeral I had been to was Ben's. That darkness we faced later. We walked until we got to the river, where the crowd disbanded. The woman manning the loudspeaker thanked us all for joining and the older people in the crowd touched their hearing aids thinking the feedback was a problem with their own hardware. It happened to be a Tuesday so we made our way to the bench, covered in a soft, green fur egged on by autumn. I don't come here enough, my husband said.

August was my worst month for a long time because that was the month Ben got better for a few weeks. I wish it hadn't happened, because losing him in September made it even harder. His cells tricked us all, the doctor said. They weren't under attack; they were attacking each other. I'd missed a few Tuesdays because Mam and I took him on day trips on those afternoons when he seemed better; once to Tenby, once just driving around town to show him what had changed since he last went out: the bank had been painted an unexpected sky blue; how Kit Willis, owner of the pawn shop, had cut her hair short and was still wearing men's trousers, even though she wasn't helping out in the factory anymore. These transformations thrilled him. He was three years younger than me but I felt immature next to him; he had worked out how to live in the space of a few months. I arrived at the bench the following Tuesday buoyed by the rich smell of the August grass and Ben's good news; he detected this new energy. We never exchanged names, but we knew how to name each other's feelings. You are happy, he said, and I told him about Ben's progress. You don't look happy, I said. His skin was waxy and his lips were cracked and dry like the summer ground. His nails were down to the quick as if he'd been panning for gold on their beds. Do you have anything to eat? They are still trying to poison me, he said, paranoid about the cooks at the Court. How can you tell? I asked. They want me dead. He said he hadn't eaten properly for weeks. I gave him my only liquorice.

There is now a carpark next to the town castle. My husband and I call it the moat as it separates the stone ruins from the meadow below which stretches towards the river. We often drive there just to park up and look down on it all. To the untrained eye, the river looks the same as it always did, but from above in the car park it is more vibrant, a shot of rust cutting through the grass. It has helped us focus over the years and we have come here to talk when we can't talk at home. It is where my husband told me he lost his job; where I told him I almost had an affair; where we decided we didn't want another child. We say these things looking through the windshield down onto the meadow, onto the flowing water, and it is like we are placing them in the current and sending them off downstream. There they go, there they go, there they go, they're gone. The moat is also where I told him about my afternoon meetings. He laughed when I told him, which surprised and irritated me. How could you not have known? he said. Everyone knew he was here. I didn't know until I knew, I told him.

I let the Nazi on the bench put his hand on my leg three times, I did not say.

When I found out, I dropped another glass in the club and another man fell to the floor shouting. It was September and I remember wearing Ben's jumper for my shift as the air had developed a chill and I liked the smell of it, of him. It was tight on me but it did the trick. Ben did not need jumpers in the stifling heat of the hospital. A guard stood by the bar in uniform; he was good-looking, but he didn't look at me, even when I pinched my cheeks. Everyone listened to him, transfixed. And every morning, the guard said, Hess makes his nurse taste his food. Thinks it will kill him. Thinks the walls have arsenic in them. When he arrived, we all lined up for him like he was the Queen. They call him The Kaiser. Can you believe that? They're getting him a dog. The Nazi. A dog. Want to keep him calm until he stands trial. They're saying he'll go Spandau. Can I have another one, sweetheart?

Go Spandau sounded like a move we'd try out on each other at the court.

I went back one last time. It worried and still worries me that my instincts did not kick in. What else in my life have I overlooked? He told me about his new dog, and I told him how our old neighbour's Yorkie was picked up by a hawk and taken away. Small thing, it was. Why would you tell me that? he said, and then he muttered something in German. It sounded like he was saying iceberg, iceberg, iceberg, as if we were sailing right towards one, unaware of the danger ahead. Iceberg. The river carried blankets of fallen leaves, a different russet to its own colour, like it had dressed up for our last meeting together. Tell me something else, he said. I don't want to hear about dead dogs. My brother is going to die, I told him, and as soon as I said it, I knew that he already had. Ben had been asleep all week and Mam hadn't left his side. Go for some fresh air, she told me, her cheek indented with the creases from Ben's pillow. We'll be here when you're back, she said. Iceberg, Hess said again. A branch, too light to hang on, twisted off the willow on the other side of the bank and fell into the water with the wind. He shook next to me, his teeth clacked. He was the thinnest he'd been. Sweets replenished, I put a small chocolate cream on the wooden slat between us and he unwrapped it quickly. Chocolate shards fell on his blue trousers, which were dotted with the sleet of a tissue. He reached into his own pocket. I focused on the water, thinking about the quickest way to get to the hospital. The smell of rot hit before I saw it. Wrapped in tissue paper beside him were bundles of food he hadn't eaten. The guard had spoken about his tantrums, his refusal to eat the Court's meals. The German opened them to reveal little horror shows of black and green and slime. It was impossible to see what they were. Broccoli? Spam? Only that they were beyond what was good and nourishing. It was death on a bench. Taste it, he said. Prove to me that this isn't poisoned. He picked up a clump of food and held it in my face. My eyes watered. I got up from the bench and ran until my chest hurt, never looking back. I didn't need to; I could imagine his face, pinched and angry, eagle's brow proud; how he perhaps threw the tissue parcels in the river, polluting it. I arrived at Ben's empty room, the mud of the meadow on my jeans. It smelled like the office, all disinfectant and stale breath. I remember how neat the corners on the bed were and how the window was open. One side of the hospital looked out on a mountain, its gorse fading.

My daughter's old babysitter checked herself in to the Court last year and I visit her every few weeks. I like having a younger friend. It is a different sort of Court now. When it is dry, Em and I sit under a tree, pretending we are free and easy, my bones dull with the chill. Age has a way of making nothing and everything hurt. Em has a boyfriend in there and is girlish and full of light. She doesn't know how long she'll stay, just that this place feels like a rest from herself. When I leave her, I walk around the grounds and past the house where he stayed. It's now a therapy centre and covered in wisteria and people walk out of there neither happy nor sad. From there I walk to the river and past the bench where there are no discernible grooves of my visits, just foil balls of chewing gum and spit freshly spat. Sometimes, I wonder if I met him at all, but most of the time I carry it with me like his parcels of rotting food.

When I was close to giving birth, I sat on the river bench, willing my waters to break. For nine months, I had cravings for lemon sherbets, and had some in my pocket. I'd had enough of being pregnant, my daughter's swinging from my ribcage, but there was something else. I thought: if I can have this baby here in this spot, I have done something. Put life where there was death. Guilt rippled through me over the years; not that I did anything truly wrong, just that I hadn't done enough. Why did you speak to him? my husband said. He's a murderer. After Ben died, I didn't go to the bench for months and, when I did return, one Tuesday, when the town streets were full of bunting and celebrations, the evacuees sent home, the bench was empty. His guard no longer drank at the club, but he did knock for me once on the chip shop window.

The labour began a few days later out in the garden while I clipped sheets to the drying line. I remember focusing on a hole left by a cigarette burn from when my husband and I used to smoke in bed. I looked through it, feeling the cool damp cotton on my cheek. I could see as far as one of the hedges that flanked the town meadow, the yellow flowers spread like butter on the land. I felt like a sniper. A warmth ran down my leg, wet and inevitable. I stood there, picturing the river on the other side of the flowers, knowing I should go inside. I stayed until I felt the first contraction, feeling the pain wash over me, pushing on through my body. I stayed until it felt like I'd travelled around its bend, out past it and beyond.

Sybilla Harvey grew up in Abergavenny and later completed an MA in Creative and Life Writing from Goldsmiths, University of London. Her fiction has appeared in *Mslexia* and was shortlisted for the Virago/Stylist short story competition. She lives in Brooklyn and is working on her first novel. This is a lightly edited version of her story, 'The Kaiser and the River', which was highly commended in the New Welsh Writing Awards 2021 Rheidol Prize for Prose with a Welsh Theme or Setting.

MEMORY CLINIC I

They will come for your memories, taking the last ones first. It could be worse. Most of our happiness lies far in the past. You will be left with a map of your life not quite to scale. Thoughts become stars – by the time they reach you they have already ceased to exist. You will plagiarise yourself and others, confuse your wife with former lovers, bang up against sliding doors, over and over. This is how life is, each decade brings new loss: your faith, your innocence, your hair, your marbles and the will to live. As for love, what can I say? Like vapour trails, miles apart, your paths were not as close to crossing as you might have thought. One day, the drugs will stop working and we can all get back to living shorter lives. Sadly, this medical advance will come too late for you.

I CAN'T COMPLAIN
(TEN REASONS WHY)

I

I have known worse nights.
Mostly on trains,
that blurred through the darkness abroad.

My body has been as good as its word.

II

They said I would be dead by now,
did some tests, then said the same again.
I tried to explain to them how
I come from a long line of statistical outliers,
plain-dwellers,
far from those for whom the bell curve tolls.

Not that there is any dignity in death,
whenever it goes down.
This one bloke, I swear,
a fart blew out the lights.

III

Take the view from my window:
even on days
when the rain flings flatways at the pane
and the sun needs a shot of Viagra,
there is always the car park
if it's entertainment I'm after.

The visitors stand fumbling change,
torn between one or two hours,
then cross the tarmac, strangling flowers.
Later, they head back with unsaid words
and sometimes bags of washing.

IV

My day is shaped now by the jobs of others.
They come intoning care, prospecting blood,
proposing tea and toast.

They offer me religion too,
though they keep it in a special room,
like X-rays.

V

The consultant and his entourage
pass through like a peloton.
Here. Gone.
Odd days,
he'll press his stethoscope against my back
or one time, a cold fifty pence piece.

I ask him, what does he hear?

I hear a man, about your years, maybe more.
He straps the Velcro on his boots,
creaks open his log cabin door,
sets out across fresh snow.

Somewhere, he falls.

I hear the empty crackle of his radio,
as rooks sketch nests in winter trees,
and starlings shift their shapes across a darkening sky.

I ask: is this a good thing?

VI

When they draw the curtains round my bed
I think of Haydock Park, where, as a kid,
I stood right by the rails,

watched one horse soar, then land and skid,
and fall and snap its fetlock.

They pulled a screen around it.
A bolt went thud and I turned to my dad
and he said it was one of those things.

Well, so is this, I guess.

VII

Please,
do not buy into the old truism
that all of this I would cheerfully swap
for the one-stop-pop of a blown-glass aneurysm.

I like staring into the chasm.
I like its edges, and its ledges and its bones.

VIII

A cold fifty pence piece!
I could have had him struck off,
thrown in the *Daily Mail*-sponsored stocks,
for that.
But we keep a gallows humour here.

Every time the call comes –
Cardiac Arrest Team to Ward H for Hotel –
that's my cue to shout:
sounds like another one checking out!

Of course,
        when it's my turn,
                someone else will have to do it.

IX

This one bloke in the next bed
had Born Welsh, Live Welsh, Die Welsh
inked on the back of his neck.
At a stretch, briefly,
I saw him do two of the three,
though by the end he grew so shrivelled
his tattooed creed became unreadable.

His death rattle was some young tyke
hauling up phlegm, as if to spit,
then losing his nerve.

I suppose that's why we're here:
to grow out of the skin we grew into,
to go out of the door we came in through.

X

This grey mince and pasta
would just about pass muster
in the midst of a war or a natural disaster,
which in a way this is.

It's been an education.
In the 83 days since my admission,
I have learned so much.
A lot of it just random stuff
I read on walls.

Most NHS fires are started by toasters.
The femur is the body's strongest
                        and its longest bone.
Sex is a level 4 cardiovascular activity,
the same as mowing the lawn.

And home.
The value of home.
I have learned the value of home.

Steven Hastings worked as an English teacher, then as an education journalist, before studying medicine at Swansea University. He now works as a hospital doctor in Aberystwyth, where he has lived for the last ten years.

STUART PICKFORD

PET

The scorpion scuttles in,
snaps the air. He's staring
at rows of nodding donkeys
on CCTV when it catches
the corner of his eye.

He grabs a broom, corners it,
curls *The Times* into a chute
and sends the scorpion crashing
down the FTSE index
into a jar of dried dates.

His bungalow's fence glints
with razor wire. On the veranda
with a Foster's, he googles them,
scorpionidae, arachnids, exoskeletals;
they walked the first world.

It calms down in the fridge,
peers through the salad tray.
The only creature to survive
The bomb on Bikini Atoll,
cold had frozen its armour.

Weekends, he drives his scorpion
to a view of the Atlas Mountains.
Parked on the crest of a wave
of sand, they watch the swallows
heading to their nests in Europe.

The scorpion laps up the heat,
thaws, winds itself up
to sting each compass point.
After it has stretched its legs,
he catches it with a fishing net.

His twin boys back home
send their own stories: how
it makes friends with a crab
and stares and stares at the sea.
They paint it red as a lobster.

The desert shifts a grain
at a time as one by one
the donkeys stop nodding
to profit. The gold is dry.
The new oil, eco-tourism.

After an hour in the freezer,
he packs the spiky scorpion

into a toilet bag with ice;
fears its shape on the X-ray
going through airport security.

Perhaps the boys could build
a hutch of chicken wire;
put the scorpion out to grass,
chewing over the view
of the Manchester Ship Canal.

A week later, in thick rain,
it plays dead. He disappears
into the shed. The twins
can't wait to see what he'll do:
their pet, a plastic paperweight.

Stuart Pickford is the recipient of an Eric Gregory award. His first collection, *The Basics*, was published by Redbeck Press and shortlisted for the Forward Best First Collection prize. His second, *Swimming with Jellyfish*, was published by smith|doorstop. Stuart lives in Harrogate and teaches in a local comprehensive school.

SUZANNAH EVANS

WE WERE THE LAST OF THE CREATIVE WRITING SOCIETY

we had printed 1000 magazines
and 800 of them still stood
in sealed boxes in the library

which is where we were when the troops came.
Max and I were sub-editors, Joe had done layout.
We used the library stepladder to crawl into the gap
above the ceiling tiles and stayed there six hours
with two sandwiches and a mini Twix between us.
Our classmates were marched out from lectures
into unmarked vans that waited in the snow.
We wondered if we were cowards
but we were scared of the guns, and although
we might have been hailed as martyrs
we couldn't make ourselves.
After a couple of hours a soldier came
to search the library. We could see
him through a crack in the ceiling tiles
his neat hair and unstubbled jaw.
He didn't search very hard.
He took up a copy of our lit mag
and started to read it, leaning
against a desk. He smiled once or twice.
There were footsteps in the corridor
and he threw it down
with a contempt performed for no one.
It sat like a little tent on the carpet.
His commanding officer piled all of history
and politics into a wheelbarrow
and we smelled smoke not long after.
When we were sure the soldiers were gone
we burned the remaining copies for heat.

Suzannah Evans lives in Sheffield. Her pamphlet, *Confusion Species*, was a winner in the 2012 Poetry Business Book and Pamphlet Competition and her debut collection, *Near Future*, was published by Nine Arches Press in 2018. She works as assistant editor for the Poetry Business. She was the winner of a Gladstone's Library residency in October 2019 for *Near Future*, and her poem, 'Helpline', was Poem of the Week at *The Guardian*.

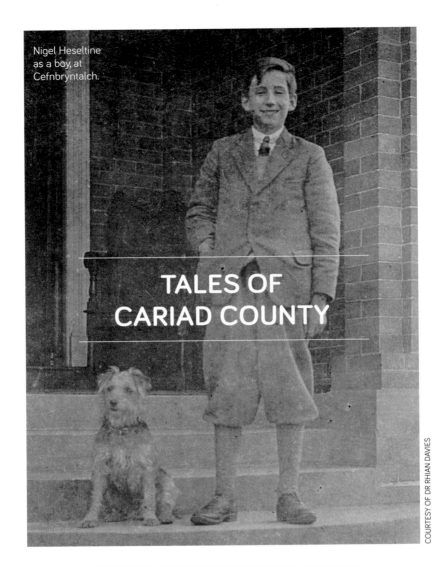

Nigel Heseltine as a boy, at Cefnbryntalch.

TALES OF CARIAD COUNTY

TONY BROWN ON THE STORIES OF NIGEL HESELTINE

In 1946, amongst the publications of Keidrych Rhys' Druid Press (based in Carmarthen) were a book of poetry, *The Stones of the Field*, the first collection of a young vicar called RS Thomas, and *Tales of the Squirearchy*, a collection of short stories by Nigel Heseltine (1916–1995).

The literary fates of the two authors has been very different: while Thomas went on to become one of our major poets, Heseltine has been largely forgotten. Yet in the late 1930s and 1940s, Heseltine was an active figure in the emerging 'Anglo-Welsh' literary scene. His poems appeared in the first issue of Keidrych Rhys' *Wales* (1937), alongside work by Dylan Thomas and Glyn Jones; two collections followed, with a selection being included in *Modern Welsh Poetry*, edited for Faber by Rhys.[1] Heseltine's poetry and short fiction appeared regularly in *Wales* and indeed he stood in for Keidrych Rhys as editor of the journal for three issues in 1939–40. This work, of course, brought him into contact with contemporaries like John Cowper Powys, Glyn Jones and Dylan Thomas, though his relations with Dylan Thomas were always mutually and vigorously antipathetic. Thomas referred to Heseltine in letters as 'nasty Heseltine' and refused to review his 'nonsense' for *Wales*, while in Heseltine's story, 'Constable's Ruin', a scene in a pub contains a drunken Welsh poet who is 'Always sixteen, always new... acclaimed in the USA and abuses his own kind... staggers with Cymric thunderbolts.'[2] Nor was Heseltine unaware of literature in Welsh; his poem, 'Dr T Gwynn Jones, 11th August, 1939', shows awareness of the episode at the National Eisteddfod at Denbigh when neither Crown nor Chair was awarded, while Heseltine's English prose translations of the poems of Dafydd ap Gwilym were published during the Second World War when he was working in the theatre in Dublin.[3]

But there is a sense in which Heseltine was always a marginal figure. His short stories portray a very different social and cultural milieu from the work of contemporaries like Glyn Jones, Rhys Davies, Gwyn Jones and Richard Llewellyn; the world of Heseltine's fiction is not the working-class streets of the South Wales Valleys but the strikingly different world of rural Montgomeryshire, stories not of the workers but of the increasingly powerless landed gentry in their faded country houses. These stories, published in magazines like *Penguin New Writing* and Woodrow Wyatt's *English Story* as well as in *Wales*, and then collected in *Tales of the Squirearchy*, are now being republished for the first time, alongside seven previously uncollected stories, in a very welcome new collection, *A Day's Pleasure and Other Tales*, edited by Daniel Hughes.[4]

Heseltine himself had been brought up in the substantial country home of his grandparents, Cefnbryntalch, near Llandysul in rural Montgomeryshire. The son of the composer Peter Warlock (whose actual name was Philip Heseltine), described by Rhian Davies as 'a misfit, loner, womaniser, drunkard and drug-taker',[5] Nigel Heseltine was deposited with his grandparents at the age of fifteen months; he later wrote that he saw his father only about a dozen times before Warlock's early death, when Nigel was fourteen.[6] The grandparents, Walter and Edith Buckley-Jones, provided the boy with stability and affection as he grew; Heseltine wrote that his grandfather 'aroused in me all the devotion of a son for his father' (*Capriol* 94) as he taught the boy the codes of behaviour expected of a young man of his social rank. To his grandmother, too, he felt he 'owed... my wellbeing and security' (*Capriol* 7), though he later became aware that she saw him in part as a substitute for her own errant son. She was a powerful personality with 'an expressive tongue' (*Capriol* 13); a friend of Heseltine later described her as 'the most domineering woman he ever met'.[7] As he grew into adolescence, Heseltine inevitably felt increasingly constrained by life at Cefnbryntalch with its attendant ritual social interaction with other neighbouring landed families:

> *It is easy to stay in your own village when you have no desires beyond its boundaries and feel safe within its maternal walls. But for those in whom the eternal striving that has created every work of man allows no rest, to grow within their village is impossible, and to be forced to stay there is death.*
> *Capriol* 132

COURTESY OF PETER WARLOCK SOCIETY

Cefnbryntalch.

One notices that 'maternal'. In fact, Heseltine is writing here about his father, but the self-identification is evident. Warlock had dropped out of Oxford; his son left Sandhurst and the military career mapped out for him. His impulse for freedom took him, at twenty-one, to Albania, his three months of travelling there providing the material for his first book, *Scarred Background* (1938).[8] Writing the book back at Cefn Bryntalch, his alienation grew more acute: 'This part of the world is dead in every conceivable way.'[9]

In other words, Heseltine is already an outsider, aware that he was essentially a foster child at Cefnbryntalch; while he continued to love the countryside, he felt himself increasingly detached from the world of the landed gentry of which his grandparents were a part. It was from this emotionally and imaginatively marginalised position that he engaged this society in his stories. Indeed, it is essential to the stance those stories take. And that society itself was in terminal decline. As Rob Gossedge has pointed out, the political power of the Welsh squirearchy had been lost under changes to local government enacted by the Liberals in the late nineteenth century.[10] The decline in agricultural and land prices between the wars precipitated further decline, a process epitomised by the estate at Cefnbryntalch itself. In the 1880s, there were twenty-two servants and two governesses and the substantial estate included several farms which were rented out, while the stables held twenty-three horses; by the time that Heseltine sold

Cefnbryntalch in 1946, following the death of his grandparents, all that was left was the house itself, 'unmanageably large', in the midst of just twenty-nine acres of garden and shrubbery (*Capriol* 30, 90–91).

As the old landed gentry clung desperately to its social rituals, they were joined in their hunting and shooting by those who had made their money elsewhere, and it is especially the pretensions of these incomers that Heseltine delighted in satirising in his portrayal of his fictional 'Cariad County'. Mr McCraw in 'A Young Night of Love', seen from the narrative perspective of a young man from one of the older families, has 'insinuated' himself into the rural community 'after some world war, having made quantities of profitable towels for soldiers, or dry batteries or whetstones, in Oldham, Rochdale, or even Nelson.' He and his wife (whose dropped aitches are carefully noted) have built Plas Parrott, pretentious and too near the road for 'a gentleman's house'. In 'Flaming Tortoises', the McCraws join in the local hunt. The Mochyn Hunt, though, is not of long foundation, has only six horses and they have never caught a fox. They charge across the countryside to the tootling of the horn of Mr Puke, 'five days a week at his desk in Liverpool, but a jolly purple-faced squire on the sixth.' The hunt descends into chaotic farce when into the chase rides young Mr Thwaite, dressed in 'loosely baggy trousers and Turkish slippers' and mounted on a camel borrowed from a touring menagerie. Thwaite, whom the huntsmen recognise as having been 'so drunk at the County Ball', appears in a number of stories, especially the more comic, farcical ones. Usually an irreverent outsider, not signed up to the codes of the gentry of Cariad County, he is in many ways Heseltine's comic alter ego.[11] Though Thwaite is not a central character in 'Milk of Human Kindness', the narrator still registers the general view in local society that 'He has not acted with *esprit de corps*.... Thwaite is a disgrace[,] and a good family too.' In the chaotic election in 'Gothic Halls', Thwaite has 'been driving a car for the Blue Cause and giving lifts to Socialists in secret.' 'Cam Vaughan's Shoot' culminates in the blackest of farces as the working-class loaders and beaters release their long pent-up hostility towards their landed employers by turning their guns on them before marching off in triumph to occupy Cam Vaughan's mansion, Parc Gweledigaethau-Sais. Thwaite escapes from the carnage by climbing an oak tree from where he 'fired at both sides impartially'.

The episode, and other moments in these stories of dark farce, containing flat, somewhat cartoon-like characters, are reminiscent of the zany, farcical tones, complete with occasional violence (potential or actual), which we find in 1930s non-realist texts like Rex Warner's *The Wild Goose Chase* and *The Aerodrome,* Edward Upward and Christopher Isherwood's Mortmere stories and some of Auden's early work. That uneasy decade, in which Heseltine grew to maturity, was shadowed not just by current international tensions but also by earlier conflicts. Daniel Hughes points out, in his introduction to the new collection, that as the world plunged anew into war in 1939, Heseltine writes in an editorial in *Wales* of 'the catastrophe which has been our nightmare since we first heard from our fathers and elder brothers of what war is', and these stories are frequently haunted by memories of 1914–18 and the wider loss of certainties those cataclysmic years brought about.[12] Sometimes such memories are fleeting, but they are an inescapable part of the world of these stories. Beth, the narrator of 'Break Away if You Can', recalls in passing as she speaks to Evans, the local farmworker, that he had 'charged with a bayonet in France like my brother'. In 'Homecoming', the people in the local church buy their parish magazine 'under Mr Robert's uncle's cross from Flanders, decorated with a button or two from his coat'. As Thwaite rides his pony as a young boy in 'Data on the Squirearchy', he is looked after by an ex-soldier who had served at Gallipoli. In the same story, the young men hang around of an evening in the middle of the village by the clock which is also the war memorial, 'the memorial to Our Glorious Dead', but the narrator bleakly details the reality of what the memorial signifies: 'carved names representing bones and unlived lives'. When the decline of the Thwaites' estate necessitates, as it had at Cefnbryntalch, the sale of the woodlands, the image the narrator uses feels almost inevitable: 'All the oak has been cut, and five hundred acres of the former estate are a desert as if shells had been dropped there.' Mr Thwaite père was seriously wounded in the War – that has left 'a hole in his head and limps' – and in a sense his condition almost emblematises the estate's decay, though, given his status in the area, he continues to be a JP and serve on various local committees, much as Heseltine's grandfather had.

Thwaite and his father reappear at the garden party which opens 'The Life and the Burial', one of the most striking of the stories, though the father, lame and 'trepanned from the war of '14, and thrice decorated', dies during the party. The local society – 'Lord Lieutenant, Chief Constable, High Sheriff… a baronet, two knights, many gentlemen' – gather again for his funeral. The burial sees him consigned 'to what Mr Bach [the vicar] will call "rest"'. But there is no spiritual comfort here: the coffin is placed, the narrator, sardonically and resonantly, comments, in a 'trench in the earth', which will 'bring about the collapse of his wooden coffin and the decay and absorption of the flesh of his body.' Nor is there any vision of the spiritual life hereafter in Mr Bach's address: 'And the empty man… shall ring against the empty man, with a hollow sound.… And that which is empty shall remain empty. And that which is full shall be poured out over the emptiness of the land.' For these stories, at times, transcend social satire per se and engage something more profound. They ultimately portray a world empty of faith in any transcendent reality, a post-1918 spiritual wasteland, in which 'nothing is fixed or predictable'.[13] The landed squirearchy cling to their social codes and rituals with an anxiety born of an undefined awareness of the hollowness beneath, and of a very 1930s nostalgia for how the world used to be: '"In my day," Mrs Golos-Williams remarked, "There was a band at garden-parties, dragoons or guards, men with long moustaches… We had frilly parasols"' ('The Life and the Burial').

By no means all of the stories in *A Day's Pleasure* employ this farcical technique, however. Two of the stories, 'Skirt in Long Strips' and 'The Word Burning', are somewhat enigmatic fables, akin to the sometimes nightmarish fabular stories which we find in the earlier work of Dylan Thomas and Glyn Jones. Here again, though, there is a disturbing sense of lost faith. In the latter story, echoing Heseltine's memories of his grandmother in her last years at Cefnbryntalch, an old woman, alone in a big house with her servants, is clearing and burning the detritus of her past: 'some of the hundreds of bunches of letters, some of the ten thousand photographs... the dead visiting cards.' Amongst these she burns 'all the figures of Life: life as love, life as action, life as happiness'. Finally, she burns 'the Word': '"Where are your angels?" asked the old woman... "And your Christ? Your Death and your Life?"' At the end of the story, the fire goes out 'and they were left in darkness'.

Other stories are more realistic in their narrative technique, and some of these are infused with far more intricate levels of feeling than the more farcical stories, emotions which manifestly have their roots in Heseltine's complex feelings about Cefnbryntalch and the area in which he was brought up: the sense of alienation and frustration, interfused with nostalgia for the countryside itself. Two of these more realistic stories, collected in *A Day's Pleasure* for the first time, are amongst the most successful stories in the book. In 'Break Away If You Can', we enter the stream of consciousness of a woman who labours with her mother, who is 'getting old, tired, thin', to maintain their increasingly rundown farm. As the woman walks the wet fields, conscious of her old mac and 'hair like dirty string' and aware that she is sliding into middle age, she remembers her father, the parties of her teen years and the promise of love with one of the local boys. But it has all come to nothing. As she now looks across the wet landscape, she reflects: 'At twenty I looked east across those same hills to everything in the world and it was all open to me: all the love and the riches and the joy I read about, was for me. But I never crossed over.' It is a bleak and utterly

Nigel Heseltine.

convincing study of loneliness, frustration and entrapment. Idris Brain, the narrator of 'Homecoming', *has* got away and made what, in material terms at least, seems to be a successful life for himself in the USA. Now, returning to the scenes of his youth, he stands outside the gates of Llwyn y Brain, the estate his family had lost in the eighteen century; like the other local estates, it has been sold, and the titled landowners he remembers from his youth are dead. He recalls the days of his boyhood on the small family farm and his beloved nurse, Hannah. He has made money – he is driving a big American car – but emotionally he has been less successful: 'I come back to my country as I left it, alone…. How could I give away my heart to a woman… when it was buried here among the woods and damp pastures and the little rounded hills?' Ultimately, it seems clear, he has never really escaped Cariad County: 'And now when my eyes are shut I see it all, and when I open them I see only the empty beautiful valley, empty for me, beautiful for everyone, through my wretched tears.'

'Rich Relations' is more directly autobiographical: the young man has come back to the large country house which his widowed mother, alone but for the servants, is struggling to manage. The impoverished son, labouring at his creative career in London ('some of my work is good; my work will live after me'), needs to borrow money from her. The narrative is presumably directly based on Heseltine's own increasingly difficult relations with his grandmother, though perhaps infused, too, with what he knew of his father's interactions with his parents. At the same time, underlying the story is, again, an aching nostalgia for the surrounding countryside, the landscape of Heseltine's youth: 'Over the stable roof, a pale blue patch in the sky; the yard was dark; rooks cawing and flying back to the woods around. He listened to the rooks and breathed the good air smelling of leaves and grasses.'

After these stories, Heseltine wrote no more fiction. Instead, having sold Cefnbryntalch in 1946 on the death of his grandmother, he travelled the world, working in overseas aid in over thirty countries, mainly in Africa and the Pacific, before settling, in his final years, in Australia, where he died in 1995.[14] Meanwhile, back in Wales, *Tales of the Squirearchy* went out of print and his writing was largely forgotten. One hopes that this new collection will bring about a new evaluation of Heseltine's fiction; it deserves it.

Tony Brown is Professor Emeritus in the School of English Literature and co-director of the RS Thomas Research Centre at Bangor University. The founder-editor of *Welsh Writing in English: A Yearbook of Critical Essays* (1995–2007), he has published widely on the English-language literature of Wales, especially on the work of Glyn Jones (*Collected Stories*, 1999) and of RS Thomas; his study of the latter in the Writers of Wales series was re-issued by the University of Wales Press in 2013.

A Day's Pleasure and Other Tales: Selected Stories of Nigel Heseltine, edited by Daniel Hughes, is published by Parthian in October and is available to pre-order now.

Endnotes

[1] *Modern Welsh Poetry*, ed Keidrych Rhys (Faber, 1944). Heseltine's two collections were also published in London: *Violet Rain* (Latin Press, 1938) and *The Four-Walled Dream* (Fortune Press, 1941). A detailed bibliography of Heseltine's work, compiled by Rhian Davies, appeared alongside her path-finding biographical essay as 'Scarred Background: Nigel Heseltine (1916–1995), A Biographical Introduction and a Bibliography' in *Welsh Writing in English: A Yearbook of Critical Essays* Vol 11 (2006–2007), pp69–101. He is the co-editor, with Jason Walford Davies, of *Too Brave to Dream: Encounters with Modern Art* (Bloodaxe, 2016), a collection of previously unpublished ekphrastic poems by RS Thomas. I am grateful to Rhian Davies for providing me with the photographs which accompany this piece.

[2] See Thomas' letters to Vernon Watkins (1 Sept, 1939, 29 Sept, 1939) and to Keidrych Rhys (8 May, 1938) in Dylan Thomas, *The Collected Letters*, ed Paul Ferris (Dent, 1985), p404, 418, 295. 'Constable's Ruin' is in Nigel Heseltine, *Tales of the Squirearchy* (Druid Press), p97–111.

In reviewing Thomas' *Twenty-five Poems* in *Wales* 2 (August, 1937), Heseltine commented that 'The richer products of his imagination roar away in unrestricted floodtorrents and leave only chirpings and scrapings of intelligibility.' But the review overall is far from wholly negative. Heseltine finds some of the poems in the collection 'hold more "material" than whole volumes of some modern poetry' and that *Twenty-five Poems* may be important 'as a portent'.

[3] The poem was collected in *The Four-Walled Dream*. The Dafydd ap Gwilym translations were published in Dublin by the Cuala Press, 1944, and republished as *Twenty-Five Poems by Dafydd ap Gwilym* (Piers Press, 1968). On Heseltine's time in Ireland, see Rhian Davies, 'Scarred Background', pp82–84.

[4] *A Day's Pleasure and Other Tales: Selected Stories of Nigel Heseltine*, ed Daniel Hughes (Parthian, 2021). The texts of the seven previously uncollected stories are those published in various journals in the 1940s, enterprisingly tracked down by Daniel Hughes. These stories were to be included in a second collection, *Tales of the Landless Gentry*, which was never published. Heseltine returned to these stories in the 1990s and made extensive revisions but these revised versions have not been published. It is the typescript of these revised texts which are quoted in M Wynn Thomas, '"A Grand Harlequinade": The Border Writing of Nigel Heseltine', *Welsh Writing in English: A Yearbook of Critical Essays*, Vol 11 (2006–2007), pp51–68.

[5] Rhian Davies, 'Peter Warlock in Montgomeryshire', *Transactions of the Hon Society of Cymmrodorion* Vol 14 (2008), pp144–61. The identity of Nigel Heseltine's mother is uncertain. It had been assumed that she was a model, Bobby Channing, whose nickname was 'Puma'. But Heseltine himself, in a memoir of his family, asserted that his mother was an unnamed Swiss lover of his father; see Nigel Heseltine, *Capriol for Mother* (Thames Publishing, 1992), pp106–111 (*Capriol*).

[6] *Capriol* 7. Warlock died in mysterious circumstance in his gas-filled London flat in 1930.

[7] Rhian Davies, 'Peter Warlock in Montgomeryshire', p146.

[8] *Scarred Background: A Journey Through Albania* (Lovat Dickson, 1938).

[9] Letter to Keidrych Rhys, 12 November, 1937, quoted in Rhian Davies, 'Scarred Background', p77.

[10] Rob Gossedge, 'Tales of the *Boneddigion*: Nigel Heseltine's Gentry Context', *Almanac: Yearbook of Welsh Writing in English*, Vol 13 (2009), pp55–80 (p55). For the historical background, see Herbert M Vaughan, *The South Wales Squires* (1926, Golden Grove Editions, 1988).

[11] In 'Data on the Squirearchy', for instance, Thwaite's father has had to sell much of his 4,000-acre estate, and only 30 acres remains.

[12] Nigel Heseltine, 'Now and After', *Wales* 10 (October, 1939), p254.

[13] Samuel Hynes, *The Auden Generation: Literature and Politics in England in the 1930s* (Bodley Head, 1976), p35.

[14] See Rhian Davies, *Scarred Background*, pp86–89.